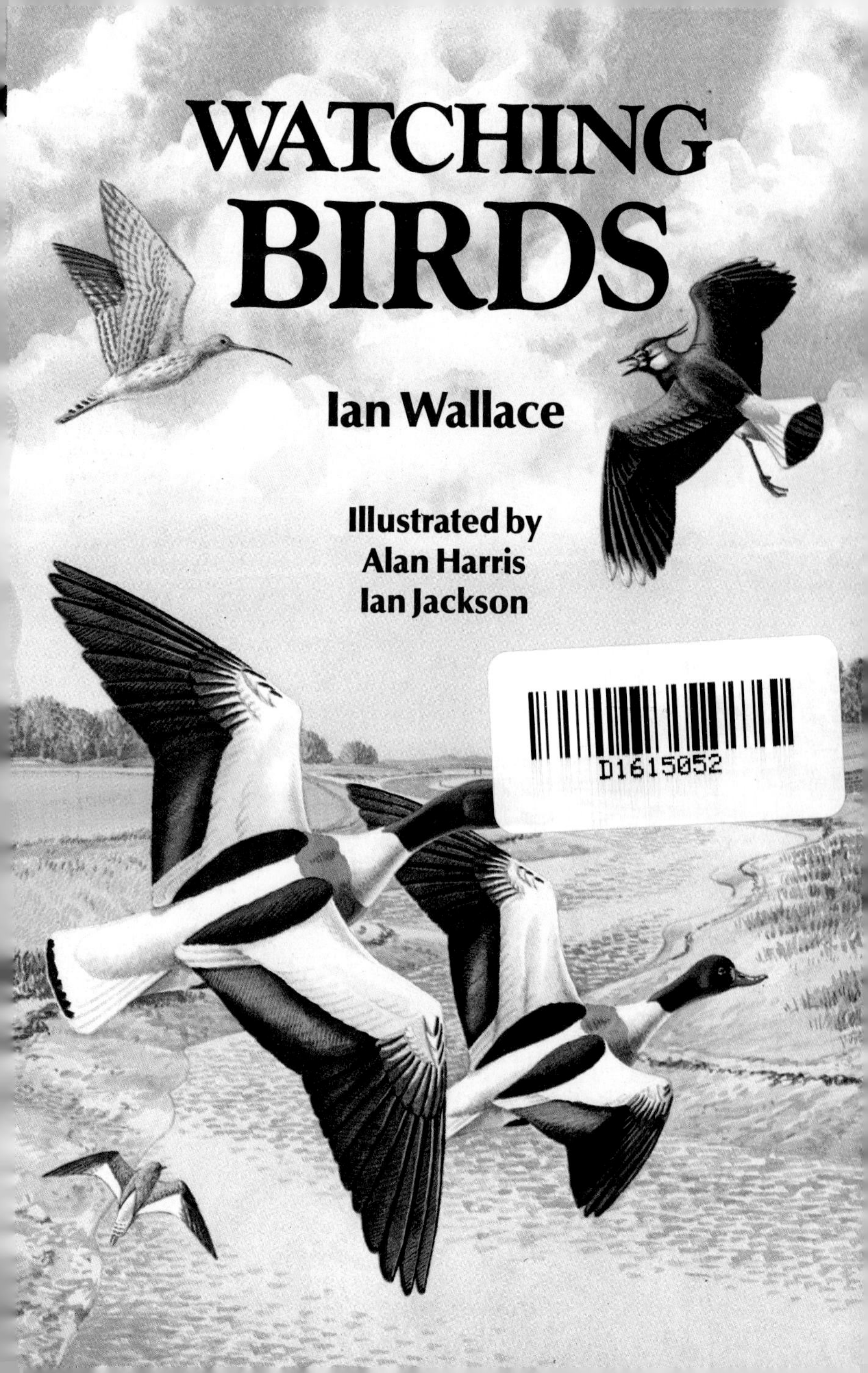

WATCHING BIRDS

Ian Wallace

Illustrated by
Alan Harris
Ian Jackson

CONTENTS

Edited by Rick Morris
Designed by Caroline Hill
and D.I.M. Wallace

Additional illustration by Andrew Ingram

First published in 1982 by Usborne Publishing Limited
20 Garrick Street, London WC2E 9BJ

Made and Printed in Great Britain
by Blantyre Printing and Bookbinding Ltd., London and Glasgow.

INTRODUCTION

Birdwatching is one of today's fastest growing pursuits. Literally millions of Europeans own a bird identification book and in Britain at least half a million people belong to the groups and societies that monitor the fortunes of birds and protect the increasingly precious habitats that they share with us.

This book is about getting to know birds and studying their ways of life. The world of birds is an exciting and fascinating one, full of endless questions and sometimes surprising answers.

For a start, where should you look to find birds? The section on reading habitat gives a lot of clues on how to look at a landscape and pick out the areas that are rich in birds. Once you know how to find these areas you will come across all sorts of bird behaviour that will set you thinking.

You may find a bird roost and want to start counting and identifying the birds that come in. Once you start looking at birds questions will spring to mind. Do blue tits, for instance, feed on the ground and right up a tree as far as the topmost branches in your area? Are great tits feeding in the same places? How do gales affect flying birds? Which species migrate through your area and in which direction are they going? You may have mallard and tufted ducks on a nearby lake. How are they both able to feed on the same area of water? Why isn't there competition between them? And what are skylarks doing on your local football pitch? This book suggests ways of finding answers to these and many other questions.

If you are looking for ideas to start you off on the study of birds, this book is full of them. There's a lot of information on how to watch birds and the techniques you can use to study bird behaviour and to survey bird movements and populations.

The studies suggested here do to some extent follow on, one from the other, but you can, of course, pick those you are most interested in.

If you come across a term you do not understand, look it up in the index. It may have been explained earlier in the book, usually on the first page listed in the index.

A careful observer watches a wheatear feeding its young, without disturbing the birds.

STARTING OFF
Identifying birds

In the next few pages I deal with the basic principles of identification, but the real art is, as with most skills, largely a matter of practice – and that is up to you.

There are about 8,500 species of birds in the world and Europe has 725 of these, grouped in families. (The relationship between families and species is explained more fully on page 16).

The aim of identification is to recognize and name an individual species. For practical purposes you need to narrow a bird down to its family group. This will leave you to select between a limited number of species to make the final identification.

The first step in this process of elimination is to get to know the different families. An understanding of the relationships between them will help.

Scientists have arranged the families (and the species within them) in a "systematic order", placing related families close together. There are several accepted systematic orders, each slightly different, but basically they all start with the families that evolved first and end with the most recently evolved.

Most field guides (identification

▼ Birds are descended from prehistoric reptiles. Fossil remains of Archaeopteryx – the earliest known ancestor – clearly show feathers on wings, body and tail.

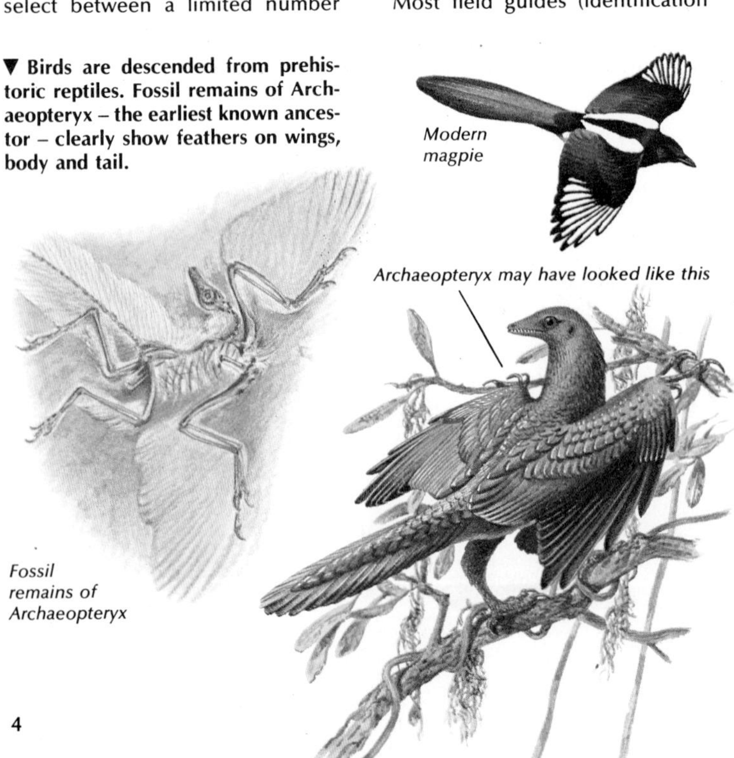

▼ Below are birds from eleven different families. Recognizing family character – size, shape and structure – is the first step in identification.

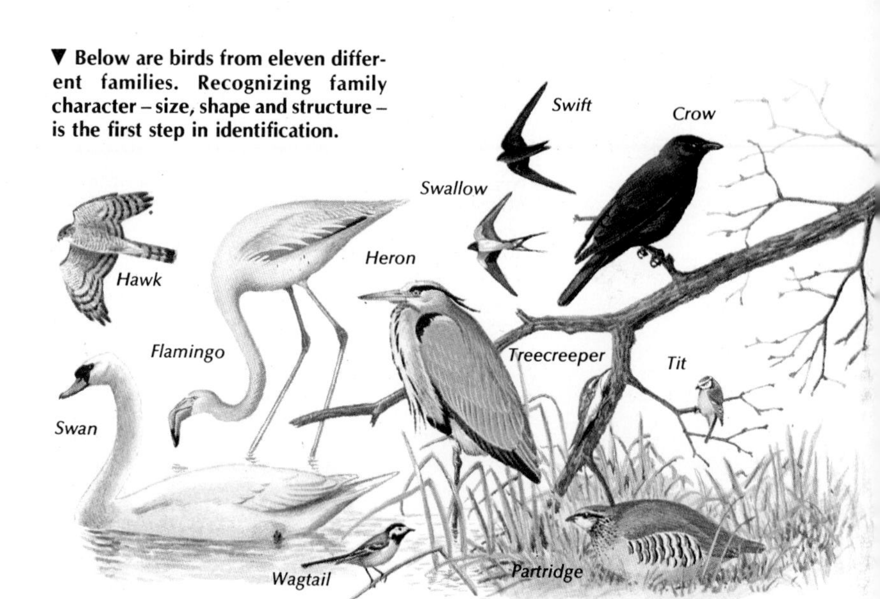

books) follow one of the systematic orders. So, study the illustrations and descriptions in a field guide (more information on field guides on pages 42 and 63) and you will start to become familiar with the characteristics of each family.

What to look for in the field

There are four main types of difference that will enable you to identify a bird. Firstly *general character* or *"jizz"* (the bird's personality, structure and actions), secondly *plumage* (the coloured patterns or "feather map"), thirdly *voice* (the calls and song) and fourthly *behaviour* (both the individual and social acts of the bird).

Make notes on all these things and you will have a good description from which to identify the bird.

▼ Plumage patterns within a family are usually quite different – as with these three tits.

Seasonal changes in bird population
An important aid to bird identification is a knowledge of the annual cycle of bird events. Each season brings a change in dominant weather, affecting the safe cover and food available and, consequently, the bird population. Knowing what to expect is therefore important.

Resident birds move to different areas during the year, migrants arrive and leave, and vagrants can turn up at any time. So be ready for birds that have flown across the Atlantic from America and others that have struggled all the way from Siberia.

All in all, bird identification is a big subject, and a disciplined approach is crucial to solving its many fascinating problems. You will find it helpful to read carefully the later sections in this book, such as "Learning key species" (page 16).

▼ Birds on the edge of a wood in summer (left) and winter (right), showing how the bird population in a common habitat changes with the seasons.

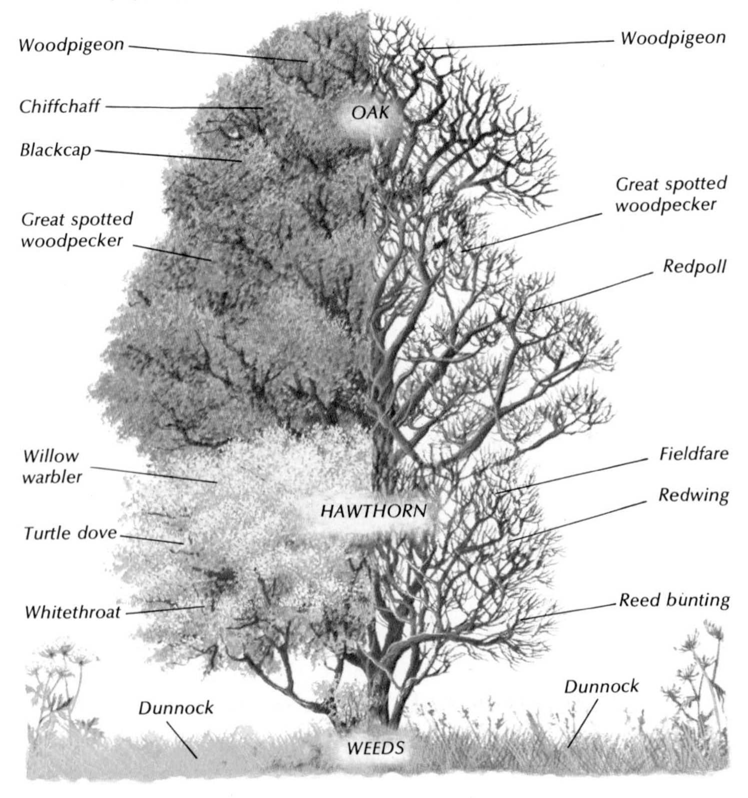

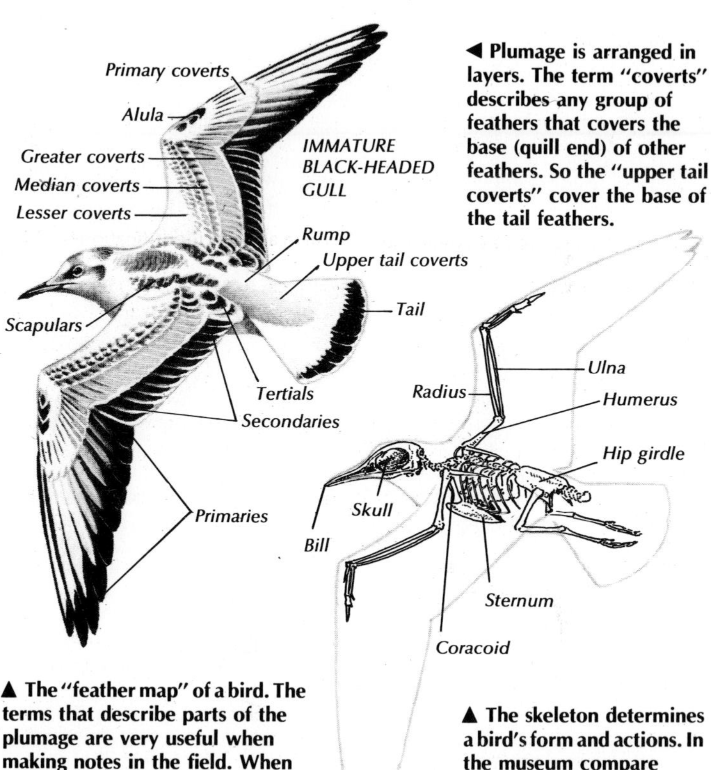

◀ Plumage is arranged in layers. The term "coverts" describes any group of feathers that covers the base (quill end) of other feathers. So the "upper tail coverts" cover the base of the tail feathers.

▲ The "feather map" of a bird. The terms that describe parts of the plumage are very useful when making notes in the field. When looking at birds in the zoo note where the wing feathers lie when the wing is closed.

▲ The skeleton determines a bird's form and actions. In the museum compare skeletons and see how they relate to a bird's shape and its way of life.

Taking a close look at birds

Dashing out with a field guide open in one hand and binoculars clutched in the other is the sure way to make immediate mistakes in bird identification.

A less frustrating way to start would be to visit two good places to see birds: your local museum and the nearest zoo. There you can have a good look at the birds with an opportunity of close study for a long period that is hard to get in the field. Try to visit them with an experienced birdwatcher and learn as much as you can from the museum's stuffed specimens or the zoo's collection of captive birds.

Remember to look at skeletal structure (in the museum), and plumage contours or the overlay of feathers (at the zoo), for together these, with the bird's muscles, determine its visible form and actions. Try to define what you see and so develop the invaluable habit of constantly cross-referring between the written word and the living bird. Start by taking notes on the birds you observe and compare your notes later with the descriptions in your field guide.

Approaching birds

To get close to birds – and have the wonderful thrill of a live, wild, flying animal at ease before you – you have to accept the role of hunter and practise fieldcraft, until its various rules are second nature to you.

The more obvious rules in stalking are quietness and careful movement, unobtrusiveness (using every scrap of cover) and camouflage (avoid gaudy anoraks), and steady concentration on the bird(s) ahead. Less obvious but equally important factors are the angle of maximum light (preferably kept to one side or behind you), the choice of sheltered and comfortable observation points (watering eyes see only blurs!) and patience. A sudden charge will have only one result – the fast retreating rear end of an escaping bird.

The alternative to stalking is to settle yourself down in a bird-rich habitat and let them come to or past you. These days bird reserves are surrounded by hides (wooden shelters with observation slits) and a watch from one can be spellbinding, so close do the birds approach. Hides are, however, not essential to the "wait and see" tactic; and the observer soon learns to vary active stalking with passive waiting, standing in shadows, sitting below foliage or next to a bush.

It is important to realize that unless you crash about like a buffalo, even shy birds usually return quickly to the spot where you first saw them. So a quiet wait by a sunny, sheltered wood-edge or looking out onto a wide estuary will always be more productive than a trample through undergrowth or a wander along a skyline.

Do not forget your own comfort and ease of movement when approaching birds. To experience cramp, chattering teeth or a sweat drop in the eye just as an unusual bird finally comes out for inspection is no way to end a hunt. One useful tip is to have your pockets almost empty and keep notebooks, etc. in a zippered bag on your waist belt. I use an old skiing holdall and it is big enough to hold compass, paintbox, water bottle and all. Unlike the always tedious rucksack, I never feel it even at the end of a long day.

Learning how to stalk

Your first stalking ground should be a large garden or a public park. There your quarry will be used to human traffic and the errors in your stalking will be kept down to a tolerable level. Please don't start with a long chase after wild geese: save them for when you are really skilled.

First pick a target bird or flock, then work out the "most covered way" to it (by judging the presence and angles of trees, bushes, fences, etc.) and then work slowly along it (don't just walk, because you must constantly check that you are screened). Remember that effective cover need not hide you completely; the trick is to mask your own tell-tale silhouette. Don't crouch or crawl from the word go; such postures can restrict your vision and should only be used when a really close approach is essential. Always keep your eye on your target and maintain a steady pace (never rush across gaps between cover). At all times, beware of scaring birds or mammals between you and the target. Their noisy alarm is likely to ruin your stalk. Guard particularly against the snapped branch or twig. Remember, too, to pick not just a

(1) When crossing an open space, walk slowly and avoid sudden movements, then (2) check the state of the birds from behind cover. (3) This is an excellent final watch point, close to the birds and with light behind you. (4) An impossible final watch point as crossing the gap from (3) will flush the birds.

target bird but also the best point for observing it, planning to have the light behind you whenever possible.

Once your skill begins to grow, try stalking in more and more open ground and learn to use every scrap of cover and fold in the land. The golden rule in wide, flat landscapes is to avoid the skyline at all costs, even if it means going the long way round. Use patience and cunning when you pit your wits against the greatest escapers of the animal kingdom.

How to wait and see

To appreciate fully the marvels that come from patient, still observation, you should pick a place well frequented by birds, find a spot (on its edge) to spy on it, and then just wait – binoculars at the ready. It is always possible to do this on foot but standing can get tiring. So do not forget how useful a car can be as a mobile hide. I look out of my car window more and more; and in October 1980, I saw an American Wigeon – new in across the Atlantic – on a roadside pool near my home.

The sorts of habitat that reveal most birds to a patient observer are the "suntrap" sheltered edges of mixed woodland, willow- and sallow-lined pools in farmland, and reedy marshes near rivers and estuaries. Always keep an eye open for such likely spots.

Seeing birds

Most of us take our sight for granted, but once you start birdwatching you will soon realize that unaided it is not powerful enough to identify birds at a distance. A century ago the shotgun bridged this gap and most identified birds were dead ones. Nowadays the optical equipment market blooms with a huge choice of glass and camera.

Few people contribute more to this market than birdwatchers. So beware the specious offers ("Ex navy, × 32, lets you read a newspaper at 1000 yards") and make your purchases wisely. Your first will be of binoculars; never buy them in the street outside the shop, only after actually looking at birds in natural habitat. Check them for sharp focus, a bright and correctly coloured image, handiness, robustness and availability of service. It is well worth taking along an experienced binocular user with you; and be especially firm about that field trial. If a retailer is reluctant you may need to leave a deposit. Always point out that you are making an important purchase because binoculars are a working tool that you will be using for many years: they therefore need a fair field trial.

Assuming they are optically correct, the ideal binoculars for birdwatching should have four further characteristics: high magnification, good light gathering power, a wide field of view and a fast method of focussing. Magnifications of 9 or 10 are favoured by most birdwatchers, so look especially at glasses with 9 × 35 to 10 × 40 specifications.

Your second purchase will probably be a telescope. A few years ago they were long, unwieldly and heavy but now they are short, compact and handier. To use one efficiently, you really need a tripod, and altogether the full kit constitutes quite a load. So invest in a telescope only if you are going to watch birds over long distances or wish to check appearance and behaviour very closely. Remember that such an instrument is inevitably a "narrow tube" with a poor field of view. In your purchase, aim always for a sharp, bright image

▼ To check your colour perception note the colours of a bird then compare your notes against a field guide.

Male chaffinch

throughout the visual range of 20 to 60 magnifications. Once again, do not buy without a proper field test.

These days many birdwatchers clank about with binoculars, telescope *and* camera, but I do not advise a camera for beginners. A reflex camera body and at least two good lenses (up to 500mm focal length) are expensive – and there is no point in contributing to the film processing industry until you are certain that a photographic record will assist your special interests.

Sadly there is no handy kit for enhancing your hearing, a sense with even more vagaries than sight. It is important that you test it for defects and adapt your approach accordingly, taking particular care to adopt a standard form of noting bird sounds. If songs and calls become a special interest, you will probably eventually want to buy a tape recorder and a directional microphone.

Testing your eyes

As well as developing a consistent style for noting bird sounds, you will need to practise recording colours precisely. In avian plumage and bare parts (bill, legs and feet), colours vary both widely and subtly.

One difficulty here is that the same colour is often seen quite differently by two people. Try describing two or three of your local species and comparing your notes against the texts (not the illustrations) in a field guide or handbook. Look out for any colours that you don't see properly. If there are many (particularly in the red band), you should take a colour card test with your doctor and so know the extent of any deficiency.

Aim too to settle on standard colour terms. One day you might be asked, "Was it brownish-grey or greyish-brown?" Being sure which tone it was may make or break an identification claim.

However good your eyesight, your final perception of birds is frequently subject to illusions. Light and shade do play tricks with colours and patterns so always try to double check your initial impression.

Keeping notes

One of the best things about birdwatching is the memories that you will have. By leafing through old notebooks, logbooks and sketchbooks you can always relive great days with birds and, of course, the not-so-great days – the ones when you got soaked through, saw nothing *and* missed the last bus.

To start with, try regularly keeping notes and making sketches. You will soon begin to build up a real bank of information. Most birdwatchers are quite good at jotting down field notes, but why not take things a step further and write a narrative log? Your logbook can be a diary account of the day's events, with comments, sketches and analysis.

The tools of the trade

For use in the field, I suggest you take a pocket-sized, well-bound notebook and a hard-backed, loose leaf sketchbook (fairly fine cartridge paper).

▼ Below are the author's field notes on an unusual warbler. On the opposite page are sketches made on the spot. The illustration in the author's log (opposite below) was drawn from the notes and sketches and clinched the identification.

strange _Phylloscopus_ 22-9.80

seen in sycamore canopy of Old Fall Plantation, Flamborough Hd.

1st found at 1000 hrs. and watched at 50, later only 20 yards for c.30 minutes, through 10x40

attention initially attracted by piercing Coal Tit-like note - written _seweet_ or _seeveet_ - but bird soon lost, - refound by calls which allowed "tracking", as it fed incessantly in upper foliage

clearly small for a _Phylloscopus_, recalling Goldcrest in shape - showed shorter tail and less bulk than nearby Chiffchaff - flight fast and light, allowing hover (when searching undersurface of leaves)

noticeably pale below, with whitish underbody constantly catching eye before any other marking - upperparts hidden at first but long supercilium very obvious, contrasting with dark eyestripe

when bird descended to lower branches, greenish upperparts showed strong pattern - quite unlike Chiffchaff or Willow Warbler ... obvious double wing-

Smaller than chiffchaff

distinctly green above

"covered in stripes"

pale tips to tertials

?two wing-bars

prominent supercilium

crown slightly paler in centre

occasionally hovered

white below

Shape rather compact - not unlike Goldcrest

thin bill with pale base

sides of breast with faint lines or clouding

details of folded wing (close view) - cream tips to both median and greater

strange *Phylloscopus*

sycamore canopy, Old Fall plantation Flamborough Head

1000 - 1030, 29-0

in sun

Yellow-browed Warbler

Phylloscopus inornatus

Old Fall, Flamborough Head

29 September 1980

identified from field notes and sketches; finished drawing matched to Handbook description and plate

confusion species - Pallas's *P. proregulus* clearly ruled out by lack of golden crown and rump patch

The ideal logbook (you will be writing this up at home) is a hard-sided, spine-lock file with loose leaf paper. A file like this will give you space for up to five years' diary accounts and field note analysis.

Make the logbook the bible of your own observations and you will have an exciting store of memories and information that you will enjoy re-reading.

You will probably also need some companion files for record summaries (to be sent to your local society recorder), difficult identifications, particular studies and the like.

The important rule in notekeeping is to preserve not only the bare facts of counts and events but also your impressions and thoughts about them. If you can do this, your records will become a rich source for both imaginative and scientific analysis over many years. Hard as it is to write full notes after a long field day, they are the very stuff of field ornithology.

▼ Below and on the opposite page are examples of the kind of records and comments that can go into a logbook.

SCHEDULE
Night migrants in Regent's Park
April 1960

Date 4 5 6 7 8 9 10 11 4-11
Species
Redwing 4 2 6
Wheatear 1 1 2 4
Chiffchaff 2 1 1 3+
Willow warbler 9 18 5 3 10 25+
Goldcrest 1 1
All above 4 0 12 23 8 3 10 39+

Wind direction SW SE S SW SW SW WSW
Overnight rain ✓ ✓ gale ✓

NB Willow warbler fall on 8th biggest in study so far; Goldcrest on same day first in spring. Totals for warblers indicate minimum numbers passing through in five days.

NARRATIVE

12 April 1960

Most of the day was spent in the Brecks and I didn't get into Regent's Park. A chance, however, to reflect on the recent falls of night migrants which though small by coastal observatory standards have been pronounced. The first influx on the 7th was two days later than in 1959 but the willow warbler count on the 8th was a spring record. As usual in spring, the warblers were all in lakeside trees and not scattered round the count route. In spite of the overnight rain and wind, the birds showed no strain and most sang as they fed. The chorus of willow warblers on the 8th almost drowned the traffic roar for once. The last fall of willow warblers on the 11th was surprising; they must have a hard time flying through the tail of the gale - but such is the purposefulness of summer visitors eager to breed that

Learning key species

You will soon come across birds that you don't recognize. Knowing something about the relationship of bird species and families will help you to identify the unfamiliar ones. Perhaps the easiest way to look at the relationships is to see them as a tree, with the first families that evolved forming the lower branches, and the most recently evolved families the higher branches. At the end of the family branches are the twigs or individual species.

In some cases there is only one species in a family. In Europe, the wren is a prime example of a well known bird standing alone as both family and species. Small, russet, with tail cocked, voice noisy and behaviour irascible, it leaves few people confused about its identity.

In most families, however, there are several, even many species, and these may show overlaps in appearance, voice and behaviour at all times or in non-breeding plumage. These constitute the pitfalls in bird identification and you will have to watch your step among them. Undoubtedly the easiest way to separate similar species is to study the commonest one fully, so that you can spot the others "by exception" and lose no time in seeing the small but significant field characters that establish their identity beyond doubt.

Examples of common *key species* are the fulmar and Manx shearwater (in the petrel tribe), the mallard and teal (in surface-feeding ducks), the kestrel (in falcons), and the dunlin and ringed plover (in small waders). These are all non-passerine birds.

In passerines (see opposite*), first targets are the skylark, the meadow pipit, the spotted flycatcher, and (in the mob of little brown jobs that make up the warblers) the reed, garden and willow warblers and the whitethroat.

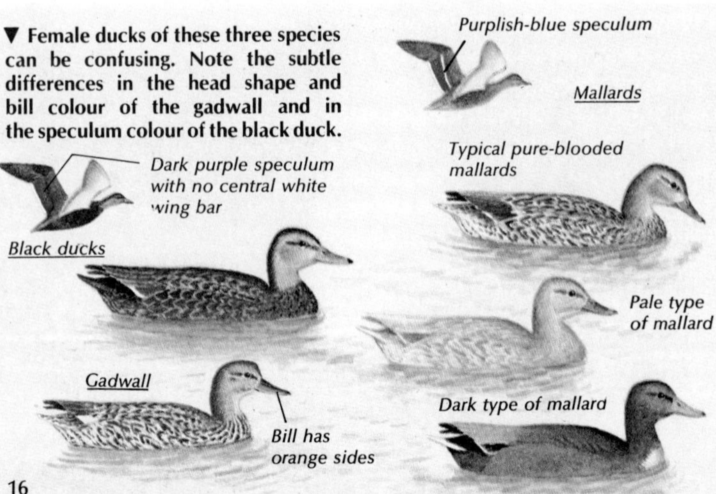

▼ Female ducks of these three species can be confusing. Note the subtle differences in the head shape and bill colour of the gadwall and in the speculum colour of the black duck.

* *Passerines form the largest order of birds (an "order" is a grouping of families). They are perching birds with their large first toe pointing backwards and the three other toes facing forwards. The families within the passerine order are among the most recently evolved (they appear at the back of your field guide) and most species have a well developed song. Birds in other orders are often simply referred to as non-passerines.*

Sorting out female ducks

Do not set yourself too severe a start in key species learning. I suggest that you begin with female ducks (see opposite) in a local waterfowl collection or on a gravel pit. Happily they are quite large birds and you can usually get good views of them.

The very common female mallard makes an excellent first subject. Not only is it similar to the female gadwall but it also sports unusual individuals which resemble various domestic strains and the rare black duck from America. Even experts are confused by funny-looking mallards, so get to know them as well as you can. Once you have done this, you can move confidently onto the stiffer puzzles of distinguishing female teal from garganey and the rarer vagrant teals. It took me 30 years to sort these out!

Separating small finches

Once you have cracked the problems of separating some groups of large birds, you can face the even tougher puzzles posed by small passerines.

One common and crucial key species is the linnet, an open country finch only too often confused – in female and immature plumages – with its upland cousin the twite and its woodland relative the redpoll. Take care: their appearances (see below) and some of their calls overlap dangerously. A mixed migrant flock of all three species, as I have seen on Fair Isle, can be the devil to sort out. Meet their challenge and your identification skills will be well established.

▼ Females of these three finches are very similar. To distinguish them, look closely at head and wing patterns.

Reading habitat

The art of "reading" habitat is to look at a landscape and pick out the features that will attract particular birds. Generally birds frequent most those habitats which support them best in terms of cover (for shelter and safety) and food (for energy). Every bird species also selects the best possible site for nesting.

Competition between species has made some of these habitat preferences sharply defined. During the seasons of migration and in hard weather, the choices of habitat may be temporarily disrupted. Even then, however, birds search for and usually find the vegetation or piece of ground that yields the best immediate living.

Generally, the more diverse the habitat (and the plants and food sources within it), the more varied its bird life. Each type of habitat has its own typical species known as a "profile". A read of your field guide will arm you with profiles of species that can be expected in woods, on heaths, and so on. What the books often don't tell you, however, is how certain plants and certain habitat interfaces provide the best chances for a close study of birds. (Habitat interfaces are junctions where two or more habitats meet.)

Which plants are best for birds will depend on which species you are looking for. The always delightful warblers, for example, favour deciduous trees and their insect life; so if you are after warblers, take a good look at any group of willows, sallows or sycamores. Particularly in

late autumn, these trees may sport not just the common chiffchaff but also the rare yellow-browed warbler, a vagrant from Siberia.

Habitat interfaces have a lot of birds because here species from different habitats meet. A slack backwater of a big river, for instance, bordered by rushes and sallows, will attract birds ranging from tits and warblers to rails, ducks and unusual waders. A careful stalk past such an area is always worthwhile and it will also be a good spot to wait-and-see.

Finding bird-rich habitats in farmland
Five thousand years ago the European countryside was largely broadleaved, deciduous woodland, but farming has modified it. Today's agricultural quilt is a patchwork, dominated by changing cropland. Scattered within this are barer high tops, woods and plantations, ancient heaths and (sadly) fewer and fewer wetlands.

Where these non-agricultural features do occur, there are miles and miles of habitat interfaces and strips along which at least two profiles of

▼ The habitat interface of harvest-time fields and woods in the author's study area. Forming an interface with the fields and woods is a stream, and inset are two species it attracts. In late summer, as the bird population reaches its peak, the open ground of the fields and the sunny shelter of the woods will support both resident and migrant species.

species abut and often intermingle. Birdwatching along such places is always more interesting than that allowed by plodding through uniform habitats.

The interfaces may be very obvious, as where a wood edge with a stream meets hedge-rimmed fields, or less obvious, as where a weedy (seed-bearing) boundary to a road offers relatively more shelter and food than tarmac and stubble.

Try to pick out bird productive areas, spotting them first from a meandering car and then checking them on foot. Having a short list of, say, five such places will speed any survey. The illustrations show one interface (pages 18–19) and one strip (above) that I regularly search in my own study area. Always be ready for the really unusual bird to pop up along such habitat edges. Even well inland, they can provide exciting encounters with migrants.

Trial and error will show you how

A frequent winter scene in farmland, near the author's home in North Humberside. A snowfall has disturbed the normal distribution of birds and they are intent on finding food from every source. Note how a weedy verge – a habitat strip – can be suddenly full of finches and buntings. Two birds of prey – short-eared owl and kestrel – are also looking for food.

to read a landscape ornithologically. A first scan over a new area should be a mouth-watering experience. Learn to think ahead and you won't be wasting time by blundering about. You'll see a lot more birds and have a good chance of finding an unusual species or two.

Studying birds in towns

If you live in a town or large city, bird habitats (and yours) will be few and much less natural. You will see fewer species but it will be fascinating to discover how far they have penetrated into the urban habitat. Magpies, for instance, have recently moved into central London (jays got there before them), herons are now breeding in Regent's Park and a pair of rooks nests within five miles of St. Paul's Cathedral. On and off I lived in inner London for 14 years and looking back, I found birdwatching there no less fulfilling than rarity-hunting in Scilly or on Fair Isle.

Exploring bird communities

Once you have worked up a knowledge of key species and habitat preferences, you will be well equipped to explore a bird community. The annual cycle of birds is dominated by the activities of summer reproduction and winter survival. The full story of these will start to emerge if you watch a diverse population through the course of a year.

Finding a bird community

Every piece of habitat attracts its own birds; so it will be best if you can find an area with a variety of cover and cultivation. This "study area" should be fairly small (200 to 300 acres) with clear boundaries so that you can view it as self-contained. It could be a city park, two or three suburban streets, the parkland centre of an estate or the surround of a lake or reservoir. If you can see the whole area from some point it will help but it isn't essential.

To start with, pick an area close to your home so that you can get to it easily. Try to visit it at least once a month through the year, or more often if you can.

Getting to know your birds

Observing a bird community will give you the chance to use all your skills of identification, stalking, note-keeping and reading habitat.

One of the most interesting things you will discover is how birds use the habitat available to them (often man-made habitats that they share with us). Which areas do they choose for feeding, drinking, preening, displaying, nesting and roosting? Why do they choose these areas rather than others? What do these areas offer them – is it food, shelter, safety, or perhaps something else?

You will see all kinds of fascinating behaviour. How, for instance, does a lapwing preen the back of its head? Well, it stands on one leg, raises the opposite wing to the horizontal and brings its free leg over the top of this wing, at the same time inclining its head backwards. Then it has a good scratch – lovely to see, hard to sketch, and it raises all sorts of questions. Does it always use its right foot? Do other waders preen in the same way?

As you wander through your study area, take time to stop and stare. Make notes whenever you can and jot down your comments, questions and impressions.

▼ To explore your local bird community stroll along a regular route through different habitats. Illustrated here and opposite are scenes you might find.

Skylarks and linnets concentrated on the less grassy patches of a football pitch. Why? Because the studs of football boots have broken up the turf and exposed an easy harvest of seeds.

Mallards feeding along the edge of a lake, with tufted ducks in the open water. Why? Because mallards are mainly surface feeders and tufted ducks are under-water feeders. Both can therefore coexist and breed on the same water.

Gulls roosting on an inland reservoir. Why not on fields? Because gulls are still essentially seabirds, wary of resting at night on land. By living in flocks they benefit from shared success in food searches.

A sparrowhawk pouncing on finches feeding near roost bushes. Why didn't it hover like a kestrel? Because round-winged hawks have developed a "close-quarter" hunting strategy designed for bird prey, not small mammals.

IDEAS FOR FIELDWORK

Studying a roost

The word "murmuration" means "a flock of starlings" and it really does sum up the busy hum of starlings as they fly in to roost.

The huge murmuration that nightly descends into Trafalgar Square, London is perhaps the best known gathering of birds in Britain. These starlings come in to roost from the whole circumference of the city and alternate sleep and chatter all night long. Generally speaking, however, our knowledge of roosting behaviour is thin and bitty. You could change this situation. So why not choose to study one of your local bird roosts?

Assessing the roost

The first step is to spy out the most likely sites, by finding and mapping the safe and sheltered coverts. Evergreens, hawthorns and rhododendrons are usually favoured, but don't ignore reed-beds and any other dense cover. The second step is to watch the sites during at least the last hour of daylight and discover which attracts birds. The third is to stand quietly by the roosts and identify and count the incoming species (see the logbook record on page 26). You will need to heighten your perception of bird calls to do this fully, since at dusk all roost arrivals tend to look like showers of black blobs. The fourth task is to stand back from the roost and try to trace the source of the incoming birds. This is not easy but it is worth a special effort,

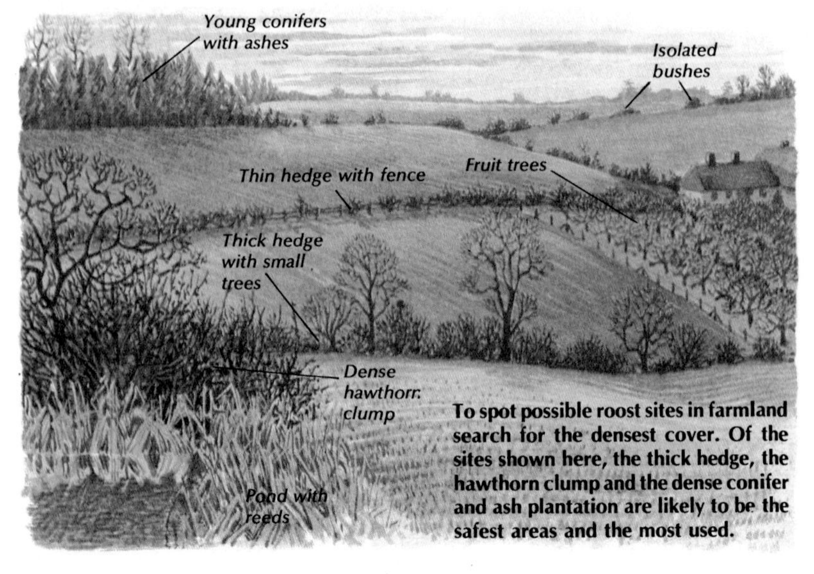

To spot possible roost sites in farmland search for the densest cover. Of the sites shown here, the thick hedge, the hawthorn clump and the dense conifer and ash plantation are likely to be the safest areas and the most used.

since it will immediately link one piece of behaviour to another. It may even tempt you up before dawn to watch the roost break up and the birds commute back in the direction from which they came.

If you can watch the roost on a regular basis you will see interesting changes in numbers and possibly in the species using it.

Surprises

As always, be ready for the occasional excitement such as a tawny owl trying for an easy meal or, as I once saw, a great grey shrike looking menacingly down at some dozy redpolls. And don't forget to send in notes on your roost watches to the local society. Few current birdwatchers bother; so your local recorder should be delighted by your special interest.

Counting the incoming birds at a roost. Some roost sites hold only one species, others attract several species. Note the type of roost cover each species favours. Numbers may vary from day to day and there will certainly be seasonal changes.

▼ A logbook record of incoming birds at a communal roost. Weather conditions and light affect roosting time. Notes on the type of cover each species uses will help you locate other roosts. The nearby rook and jackdaw roost would be worth studying. Are there other flight lines to it?

6.2.82. Communal roost in hawthorns, bramble, rhododendron and box. Cheddar Gorge. Dry, light afternoon, Sunset 1659 hours.

	1630–1645	1645–1700	1700–1715	1715–1730	TOTAL
DUNNOCK	1.	1.1.2.	1.1.	—	7
CHIFFCHAFF	—	1.	—	—	1
REDWING	2.1.6.	4.5.1.7.10.	15.11.13.8.9.12.	5.3.1.3.1.1.	118
SONG THRUSH	1.2.4.	1.3.5.1.2.	1.2.3.10.6.3.	1.2.1.	48
TREECREEPER	—	1.	—	—	1
CHAFFINCH	5.3.1.	4.8.14.	12.18.3.1.2.1.	3.	75
	26	71	132	21	250

Most redwings favoured the hawthorn with some in the rhododendron. Ditto the song thrushes. Chaffinches were concentrated in the bramble thicket and box with odd birds in the rhododendron. The treecreeper was seen to disappear into the rhododendron. At 1651 hrs. a large, noisy, mixed flight of rooks and jackdaws (500-600 birds) passed overhead in a SSW direction.

7.2.82 Same Cheddar Gorge roost. Light rain with heavy clouds building up. Daylight fading quickly. Sunset 1701 hrs.

	1615–1630	1630–1645	1645–1700	1700–1715	TOTAL
DUNNOCK	1.1.2.1.	1.1.1.	1.	—	9
CHIFFCHAFF	1.	1.	—	—	2
REDWING	4.1.3.7.10.15.	8.9.12.13.4.5.	3.2.1.2.6.3.1	1.1.	111
SONG THRUSH	1.1.2.2.4.3.1.	2.5.8.3.2.4.	2.1.2.1.1.1.	—	46
TREECREEPER	—	1.	—	—	1
CHAFFINCH	3.4.1.2.5.3.2.	4.6.5.8.12.9.	3.4.3.2.1.	—	77
	80	124	40	2	246

The heavy cloud, rain and fading light (it was quite dark by 1705 hrs) brought all the birds into the roost half-an-hour earlier than yesterday. All, bar 2 redwings, were in the roost by sunset; whereas yesterday,

Mapping starling flight lines
The bird roost champion of Europe is probably the starling. It forms enormous assemblies at dusk and these swarms – sometimes numbered in millions – spend the night in sheltered places. In open country, starlings mostly choose dense plantations or reedbeds to roost in but in this century, their suburban and urban cousins have clearly worked out that the centres of cities offer both warmth and safety.

The large starling roost on buildings and trees in and around Trafalgar Square, London was the subject of a major piece of research 30 years ago. The map below shows how the amateur observers of the London Natural History Society defined the length and direction of the flight lines of incoming starlings over the entire London area. You could do similar research in your home area and hunt out your local starling roost and the flight lines to it.

Plotting flight lines
When you see small flocks of starlings in the evening, plot a line on the map showing their direction of flight. By moving to different places on other evenings you can begin to plot several flight lines. The roost should be located where these lines meet. It will take some time and effort to define all the flight lines and how far they extend and this is probably best done with a team of people. It would be interesting, though – with the help of a car or bike – to follow one flight line yourself, to see just how far the birds fly to the roost.

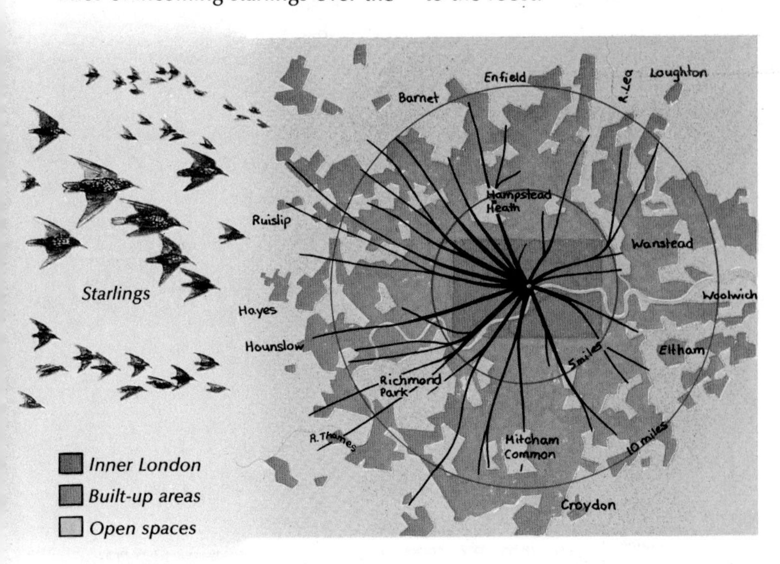

▲ **The 1952 map showing starling flight lines (in black) to the central roosts in and near Trafalgar Square, London. Some birds flew 14 miles to roost.**

Looking at tits feeding

Tits have long been the favourites of behavioural scientists, with the birds' seemingly clever and certainly acrobatic antics and relative tameness. But there is always something new to be learnt about these colourful birds. For example, how do the six common species (blue, great, coal, marsh, willow and long-tailed tit) coexist in your local woods? One way to answer this question would be to observe closely their food searches to see which trees and plants they feed on and at what heights they are feeding.

During my winter exploration of Epping Forest in 1971/72, I noticed that the blue tit was present everywhere and was (presumably) the commonest tit. It clearly found some food in most vegetation and all the way up from the forest floor to the topmost twigs of beeches. How about finding out if it feeds in this way in your area?

How to survey

The first step is to find a typical piece of mature mixed woodland (including both deciduous and coniferous

▼ Watching a tit flock. Identify the different species and count them. Then note the span of height used by each species and the type of vegetation they are feeding in. Plot this information onto a map or record sheet.

trees) that harbours tits. The second is to explore it fully and track the normal rounds of tits within it. The third is to construct a precise form for your observations. Divide the wood into areas of different vegetation, depending on the plant species, their densities and their heights. The illustration below shows a simple diagrammatic way of doing this. The fourth task is to choose several regular paths through the wood and count and map (by site and height) all the tits that you encounter along them. Keep separate records of each species to see how they differ.

Working at, say, fortnightly intervals, your data will soon build up and your perception will grow too. The fifth and most mentally stimulating step is to analyse your records month by month to see how the changing vegetation affects where the tits feed. It could be that even the experts will learn from you. Incidentally you will never be bored in a wood, for even if the tits are absent, it will be the turn of a nuthatch or woodpecker to delight you.

▼ **Final analysis of blue and great tit feeding heights in Black Plantation, from January to March 1982.**

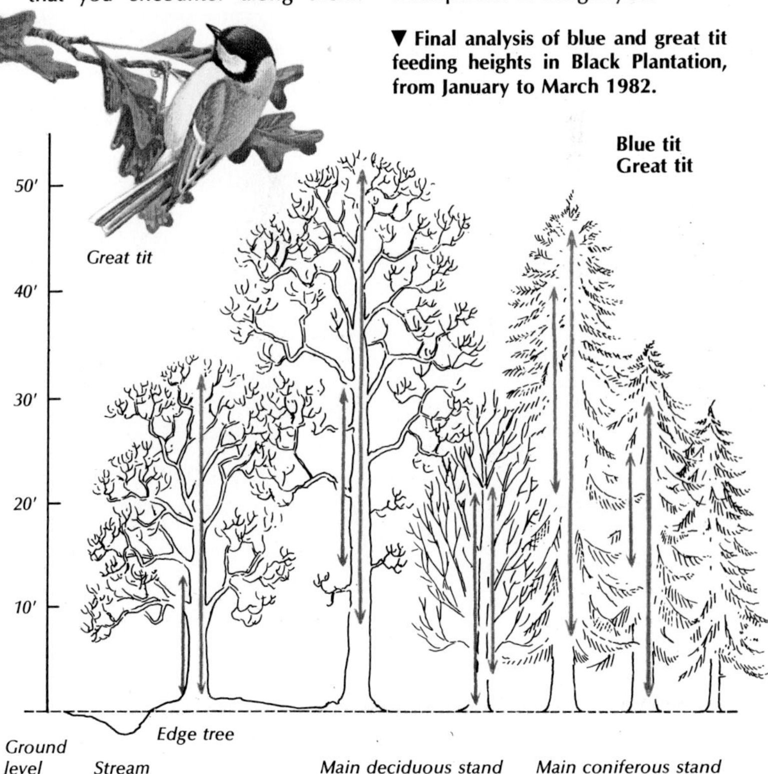

How does wind affect birds?

So envious are we of the flight of birds, we tend to believe that they have total mastery of airspace. This is not true, however, and strong, particularly blustery wind clearly inhibits wing action and aerial behaviour.

Surprisingly, I can think of no sustained study on the effect of strong wind on birds. I have tried to assess it when watching the coastal passage of seabirds and it seemed that given a wind force (on the Beaufort Scale) of 8 or above, even totally pelagic (ocean-living) species begin to have problems in maintaining station and direction.

Indeed, to watch such majestic birds as gannets turn and run before the wind is an awesome spectacle, worth seeing for the sight alone. Of course, birds surrounded by land can avoid wind stress simply by land-

Watching seabirds in a gale. At what wind speed do birds turn and fly with the wind rather than continue battling into it? Does poor visibility or rain make them turn at lower wind speeds?

ing and clinging onto something, but how strong does the wind have to be to stop them flying? And if it is raining, as well, do they stop flying sooner?

Working out the effect of wind stress
You could test these questions on two common summer visitors, the swallow and the house martin. Both of these birds feed on insects caught in flight, so they are ideal for this study.

Here are a few clues on how to start. First, get hold of a copy of the Beaufort Scale which will show you how to judge wind speed. Second, tune into the shipping forecast (on BBC Radio 4 at 0625, 1350 and 1750 hours) to find out when gales are forecast. You should be able to judge from the nearest sea area if gales are going to hit your part of the country. Third, go to a habitat where swallows or house martins feed (ponds, cricket pitches and farmyards are often good spots). Fourth, watch the birds tussle with the rising wind and note down what you see.

Check the wind speed regularly and see how this affects the birds' feeding activity. Are they feeding in an open area or using the shelter of trees and buildings? Are the birds flying low? Do they perch now and again or fly all the time? Watching their behaviour closely you will probably come up with all sorts of other questions. Are there, in fact, any insects on the wing in a Force 7 wind?

Do some background reading on bird behaviour if you can, as you'll find that knowing some of the answers will lead you to ask the right questions.

Swallows feeding in the lee of a barn where they get some shelter from the wind. How strong does the wind have to be to stop them flying?

Observing migration

Bird migration is the only mass animal movement that we regularly see, now that Europe has lost its droves of wild mammals. It is a phenomenon that is both quite astonishing and easily understood.

Bird migration is astonishing because we have to accept that birds as small as goldcrests (weighing just a few grams and with a pea-sized brain) can successfully fly over both cold mountains and stormy seas. We also have to accept that they – and all their migrant companions, from the closely related firecrests to wild swans – have inherited navigation systems which enable them to find and refind both their summer and winter homes. (Thus my own pair of swallows fly unerringly between my stable and a South African reedbed.) All these unlikely propositions have now been confirmed by extensive research, but after 40 years' experience of bird migration, I still find it totally enthralling.

Bird migration is, however, fully understandable, since it is a reflection of the seasonal ebb and flow in the food supply. As long as this food source fluctuates, then birds will react to its changes and pounce on every opportunity offered to them, whether for summer reproduction or winter survival.

The basic rhythm and some of the dimensions of bird migration were first spotted 5000 years ago but it is only in the last 30 years that ornithologists have fully demonstrated just how far birds can travel. Given their powers of flight, energy conservation and navigation, birds can shift almost from pole to pole and (in temperate latitudes) across a third of the world's circumference!

Types of migration

With such a complex phenomenon, it is not sensible to generalize too much but in most of Europe, various types of bird migration are broadly separable and can be studied by a selection of techniques and tactics.

The most obvious migratory movements are the arrival and departure of locally breeding summer visitors, the passage (generally north in spring and south in autumn) of high latitude summer visitors, the arrival and departure of winter visitors (escaping from the extremer continental climate to the east), occasional irruptions (of species suddenly become numerous or faced with a food shortage), the overshooting of low latitude summer visitors, and the vagrancy of Asian and American birds.

▲ **Many birds migrate unseen at night.**

On the western seaboard of Europe – and nowhere more so than in Britain – all these movements can become suddenly visible. Birdwatchers have learnt to look out particularly for weather conditions that produce migrants. These can be anticyclones and easterly winds that allow birds to drift west across northern Europe; warm, wet southerlies that push others north from the Mediterranean; and howling westerlies (born of Caribbean hurricanes) that blow yet others across the Atlantic.

Study techniques
The study of bird migration was most popular in the 1950s and 1960s and its study methods were most refined then. Essentially they combine two disciplines, a daily estimate of birds both grounded in or moving over a clearly delimited recording area and a related sample of birds trapped in the same area or in other areas where summer visitors are concentrated. The captured birds are measured and weighed, examined for moult and other physiological conditions and then ringed in the hope that they will be recovered at another point along their route or retrapped later at the same site.

Trapping, examination in the hand and ringing require lengthy training and you must have a permit (from a national authority such as the British Trust for Ornithology). It is illegal to "have a go"; so please do not. (See pages 46 and 48 for places to observe trapping and ringing.) In your first years, you should concentrate on the counting discipline and experiment with it in various habitats.

Bird migration is most clearly seen along hillsides, across water and on coastlines. It is most dramatic on promontories and offshore or oceanic islands but in the following pages I deal mainly with inland observation techniques.

This map shows some of the movements of birds over Europe.

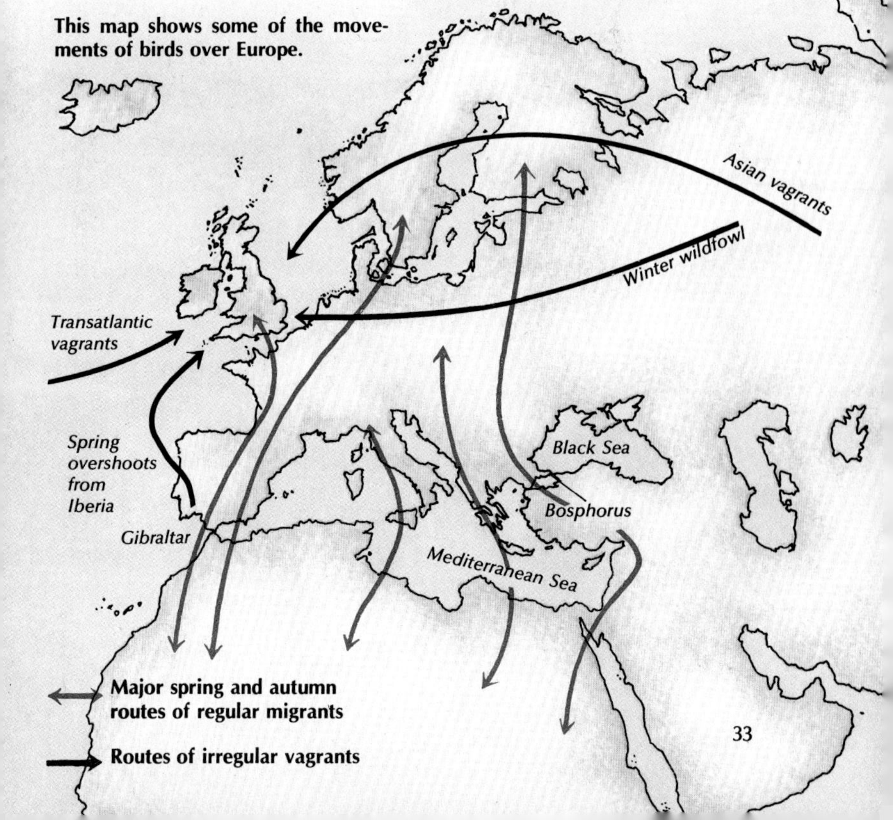

Counting migrants on the ground

During your first exploration of a bird community, you are likely to experience at least one marked arrival of migrants. Suddenly among your resident species, there will be a flush of warblers, a swirl of finches or thrushes, or, to mention a scarcer bird, a green sandpiper exploding out of a ditch.

To assess such arrivals and the subsequent departures as precisely as possible, you must first pick a sampling area or map out a counting route. Then walk through this area or along the route as often as possible – daily just after dawn is favourite – and count every bird present. Take care too to note the weather and any other associated event. By transposing your counts and notes to a daily register, you will soon develop a measure of the bird migration in your area. Examples of a logbook record of grounded migrants appear on pages 14–15.

I shall be surprised if you do not succumb to the pleasant fever of migration study within a week of starting your daily search.

▼ Migrants fly lower and are most visible when flying into or across a headwind. Here the majority of birds (97%) were flying W to NW into NW and N winds. Peak numbers occurred shortly after sunrise, tailing off as the sky clouded over.

6 November 1960 Primrose Hill, London

Wind NW, then N, Force 2–3; sky clear at dawn but clouding over, 8/8 cloud by 1000.
Sunrise 0735. Usual mile front as count base.
Not cold. h = heard not seen.

¼ hour counts starting at	0715	0730	0745	0800	0815	species total
WOODPIGEON	30 W 20 W	20 WNW 75 W 80 W	275 W 175 NW 16 W	42 W	6 W	739
SKYLARK			1 W	h 2 W 1 W 1W h	h	8+
FIELDFARE	12 NW 2 W	25 WNW 5 NW	3 W			47
SONG THRUSH	5 WNW				1 W	6
CHAFFINCH	7 W h	2 NWh 4 NW 2 NWh	4 NW 1 NW h	h 5NW h 5 W h	h 1 W 3. WNW 1N 2 NW	45+
GREENFINCH		1 NW 2 NW 3 WNW	h 1N		3 NWh 2 NW 3 W	17+
GOLDFINCH	1 W		2 WNW	1 W		4
HOUSE SPARROW	2 W	6 W	4W definitely	4 SW on the	move!	16
TREE SPARROW	5 W	1 W	2 W			8
STARLING	120 WNW 18 NW 21 SW	20 NW 15 NW	1 NW 30 NW 27 NW	12 WNW 150 NW 4 NW	SW	423
Grand totals	244	263+	544+	232+	30+	1,313+

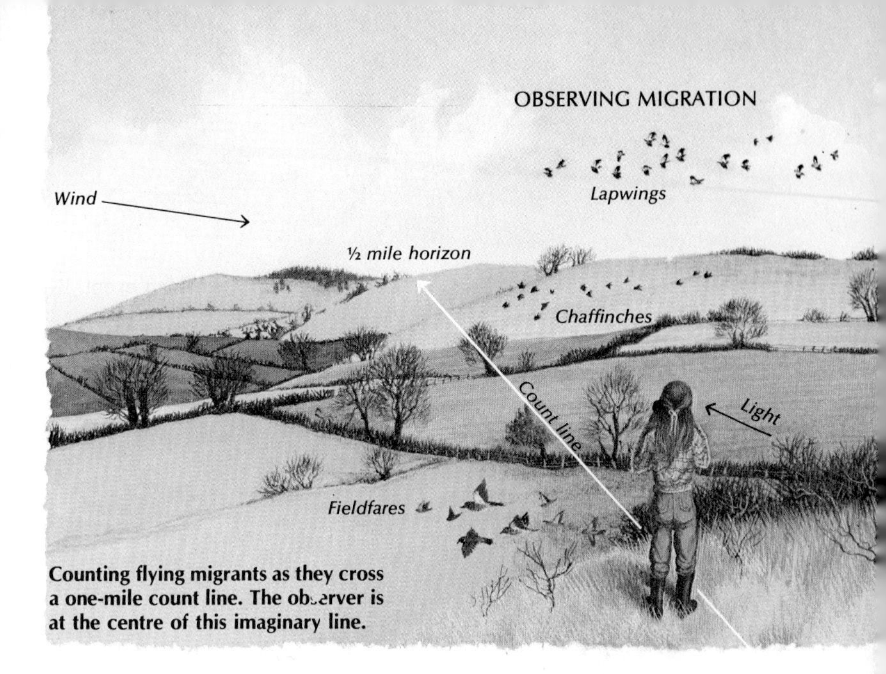

Counting flying migrants as they cross a one-mile count line. The observer is at the centre of this imaginary line.

Counting migrants in the sky
Again, during your early fieldwork there will probably be an autumn day when the sky is unusually full of birds, perhaps lapwings in twinkling flocks or fieldfares in harshly chuckling parties. The day may also be one of low cloud and northwesterly wind, the last forcing the birds to fly into it and "keep their heads down".

Getting a full quantitative measure of such movements is impracticable but obtaining a qualitative sample is well worthwhile. Your first task is to find an uncluttered viewpoint, such as an isolated hill, a valley shoulder or an open horizon.

Your second task is to establish a fixed count line (see the illustration above). Ideally this line should be a mile long (half a mile in front of you and half a mile behind you) but its length will actually be determined by the limits of your flight identification expertise. (You will need to work hard on basic plumage patterns, flight actions and calls.)

The third job is to count all the birds passing over the count line, noting the flight direction of each flock, as in the table on the left. If you count "all" the birds passing over a mile front for one hour, you will get a total of "birds per mile per hour". You can work out passage rates for individual species on the same basis. These standard measurements make it easy to compare counts from different days.

You can also assess the directions of passage of different species over your count line. Never pretend to see all the birds in the sky; concentrate most on a qualitative sample and you will soon learn what birds are flying over your area. Believe me, it is great fun. Dawn watches from Primrose Hill in London in the 1960s brought me staggering flights of thousands of woodpigeons and wonderful single birds like a lost Bewick's swan and an osprey!

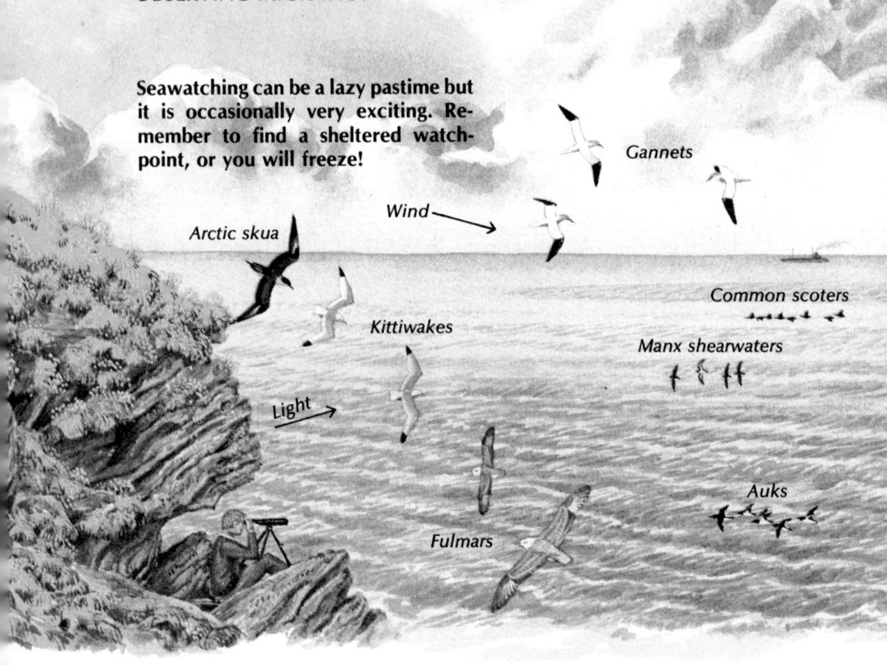

Seawatching can be a lazy pastime but it is occasionally very exciting. Remember to find a sheltered watchpoint, or you will freeze!

Watching seabird passage

As a change from the routine of inland observations, there is nothing more refreshing than a long watch over a stream of seabirds. Seawatching, as the technique is called, is a recent invention and was first developed at the most famous of Irish bird observatories, Cape Clear Island in County Cork.

What you can see on a seawatch will depend on the weather, the angle of the light (it needs to be behind you) and your height above the sea (if you are too close to sea level you will miss birds further out).

When you first start you will need some guidance from experienced seawatchers. They will be able to give you a lot of tips, particularly on identification and how to locate birds at sea. Seawatching is an art and it will take time to pick it up. The excitements can be huge but the risks of mistaken identifications are enormous.

Seabirds are made most visible during onshore gales and tend to be concentrated in passage streams where a headland or coastline angle interrupts the normally broad front dispersal of birds offshore.

So before any first attempt, you should study a map of your nearest coast and pick your watchpoint to allow a maximum of back light and your greatest extension into the water mass. Then wait for when the wind blows onshore – for example, NW to SW on west-facing coasts, NW to E on east-facing headlands or shorelines – and off you go, remembering that a dawn start is the only way not to miss something good.

25 September 1976
Flamborough Head and Bridlington Bay

ENE/ESE 6-8
Rain to 1245

I went straight to the head but apart from large rain,
I could see nothing moving at sea and only the odd
chat round the carpark. So I wandered off in the
car to check a few hedge lees, finding Redstarts,
Wheatears and, surprisingly, many Reed Buntings.
A Ruff stumbled through the deluge which was
so constant that I almost gave up and went
home. A lucky stop at North Bay at 0950 soon
convinced me that I should stay, for suddenly
seabirds were pouring past just offshore.
Clearly the near gale and poor visibility
was "trapping" them against the coast and
forcing them to turn back east under the
southern cliffs. I watched from the shelter
of the car for three hours with absolutely
splendid results and ad... alin surge after
adrenalin surge. It wa... do with the
weather: low squall... ight, and the
birds coming N, ... ount to E. At
1245 the weath... hurried
back to the he... e was still
obvious. As ... t the "sea
bird tra... t back
to the ... inutes
fron ... was
S... a
... g

25 September 1976
Flamborough Head and Bridlington Bay

	North Bay 0950-1245	Head 1300-1450	North Bay 1515-1545
Red-throated Diver	2	15	1
Fulmar	1+?1	15	
Cory's Shearwater	2		
large Shearwater	6	1	
Sooty Shearwater	1		
Balearic Shearwater			1
Leach's Petrel	36	30	5
Gannet		35	3
Wigeon	5	1	
Scoter		10	
Goosander			
Grey Plover	53	1	
Knot	15		
Ruff	12		
Redshank	3		
Bar-tailed Godwit	3	2	
Great Skua		13	1
Pomarine Skua	4+?1	7	1
Arctic Skua	68	36	5
Skua		1	
Long-tailed Skua	6+?2	7	1
Little Gull	49	26	
Kittiwake	390	150	40
Sabine's Gull		1	
Black Tern	8	2	3
Gull-billed Tern		1	
Sandwich Tern	11	15	5
...mmon Tern	12		
... Tern	21		

All birds moving into NE/E gale, unless as stated

no sign of a Manx!

included incredible flock of 50! with Grey Plover flock

2 with Grey Plover flock

7 immatures

at least 6 immatures

up to 23 on sea

P.S. White-winged Black Tern seen at head following my departure!

...ssion of surges in passage at 1015-1023,
...-1120, 1300-1320, 1400 and 1500-1510
...ciated with brightest light-brea...
...d this "exposed" tubenoses
...hind those in identifica...
...ows what was miss...

▲ An account of a great seawatch, from the author's log.

Studying bird populations

▲ **A male reed bunting singing to proclaim his territory.**

Only 20 years ago few but professional ornithologists even attempted population studies – the foundations of bird conservation – but today tens of thousands of ordinary birdwatchers confidently contribute to them.

If you have already studied bird communities and migration (see pages 22–23 and 32–37) you will be well prepared for measuring bird populations. In most European countries, ornithologists and birdwatchers have already combined efforts to map the distribution of breeding birds, to sample their numbers, to assess the mass of vulnerable groups like seabirds, geese and waders, and (from 1981) to survey the distribution of wintering birds. In addition, there are current regional surveys of the birds of scarce habitats and a host of local studies. So the choice is wide and, in most cases, full instructions exist.

You must decide what kind of population study will interest you most, then set yourself clear objectives, choose a study area and relevant study methods, and finally make a long-term commitment to the most involving kind of birdwatching that there is.

Knowing how badly conservationists need more information on the fortunes of ordinary birds, I suggest that you attempt a population study close to your home and in three parts. Aim (1) to make a census of breeding birds, (2) to sample the arrival, passage and departure of migrants, and (3) to index the numbers of wintering birds. In this way, you will be able to see how birds ebb and flow through even a small piece of ground. The rest of this section explains how to do this.

Choosing a study area

If you have let this book guide you step by step, you should already have your eye on a likely study area. If you have not, look back at page 22 and note the way of spotting one. This time round, take into account the general approach summarized above and try to select an area (and its habitat balance) that are typical of the landscape in which you live. Your study results will then be broadly relevant to the wider ornithology of your region.

Mapping a study area

You will need to use large scale maps so that you can define the boundaries of your study area and see what different habitats it has. In Britain, for example, there is a 6″:1 mile (1:10,560) series of amazing detail. This is the ideal size to use when selecting an area for study, as boundaries, buildings etc., can be clearly seen. For actually plotting the positions of birds you will normally need a larger scale Ordnance Survey map of 25″:1 mile (1:2534).

Provided you update it with any major changes to buildings, hedges and woodlands, your local 25″ sheet

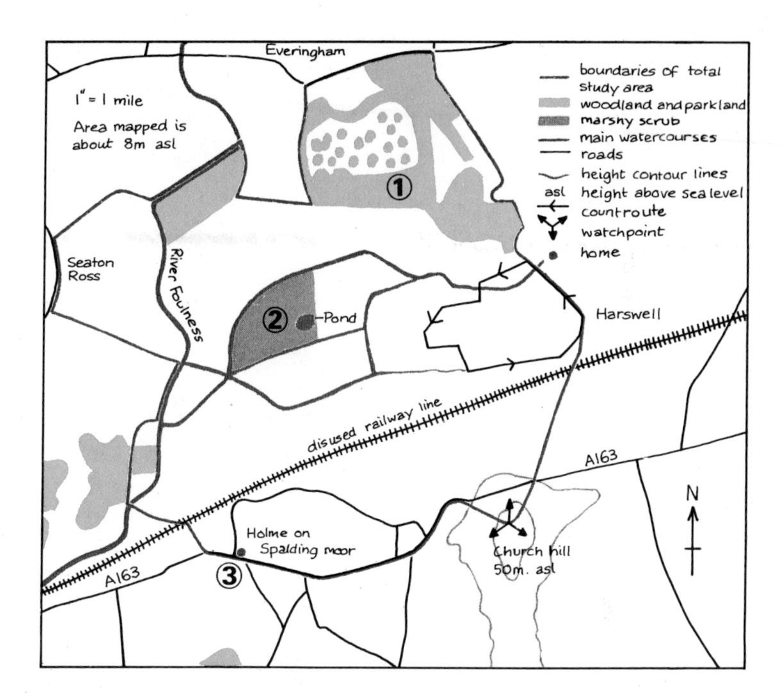

▲ Try to choose a study area close to home. This map, of standard Ordnance Survey 1" scale, shows the author's study area 19 miles SE of York. Note (1) a large woodland area, (2) a last patch of wilderness and (3) the main village. All will support bird communities which are different from those in the surrounding farmland. CBC plots can be chosen in (1) and anywhere in the farmland.

will form an excellent plan for your study. You will need to keep a master copy – to record the habitat changes and uses – and at least 20 other copies on which to record bird positions and numbers. If you use coloured pens and symbols, do not forget to key them.

Taking a census of breeding birds

Various methods exist to establish the density of breeding birds but in order to make your results compatible with those of other birdwatchers, it is sensible to use that adopted by your national conservation body. In Britain, for example, it is the Common Bird Census (CBC) which is administered by the British Trust for Ornithology (BTO).

Essentially the survey requires you to plot the precise positions of all singing, territorial male birds noted during spring and early summer in your study area. You may choose a farmland study area, for which at least 10 visits and an acreage of 200 (80 hectares) is the standard model, or a woodland one, for which 15 visits and 50 acres (20 hectares) is the usual requirement. To be of value to the BTO the survey should be carried out over a period of several years so that annual changes in

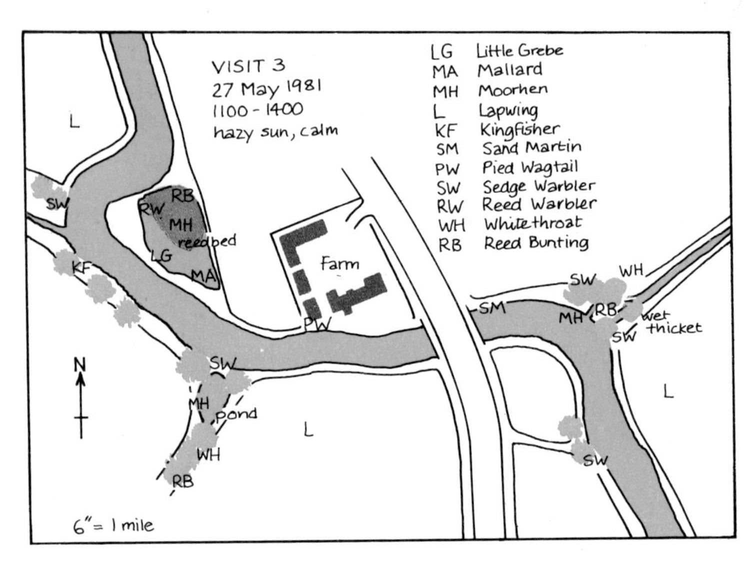

▲ **A map from the Waterways Bird Survey. Plotted on it are the positions of singing, territorial male birds, recorded on one visit.**

breeding numbers can be compared.

The CBC is never complete – for a start, some birds are more easily missed than others – but it has been well tested since its inception in 1961 and is, therefore, widely quoted by conservation bodies. It is a survey well worth doing *providing* you have the time available.

If you have a particular interest in the birds of waterways, there is an alternative breeding birds census right up your street. It is the Waterways Bird Survey (see the map above) which, like the CBC, is organized by the BTO. This survey asks you to plot the whereabouts of over 50 species dependent on waterside habitats. The model performance is at least 9 searches of a 3-mile (5-kilometre) length. Full instructions on both surveys are available from the BTO (address on page 62).

Of course, you do not have to adopt the BTO methods. You may like to start with a simpler and quicker "straight line transect count". For this, plot a line across your study area and survey along it. This will provide a sample of the breeding birds in your study area, rather than a complete census.

Counting migrant birds

The various ways of counting migrant birds were discussed earlier, on pages 32–37. This time around, you have the chance to correlate your migrant counts made along a set route or through a selection of habitats with those made of breeding or wintering birds. Birds do not move only in spring and autumn. At least some do so on every day of the year. So there is always the chance of a surprise.

It makes sense to include your migrant count route with your CBC area but if there are other bird-rich habitats nearby, say a lake, a sewage farm (always good for birds) or an area of seasonal floods, frequent inspection of these will allow you to monitor a greater variety of species. Examples of the records that can be kept of migrant birds are shown on pages 14–15 and pages 34 and 37.

▲ Redwings are winter visitors whose numbers are affected by the weather.

Counting wintering birds

A standard method for assessing winter bird populations has not yet been set, though that chosen for survey work to produce a winter atlas (started in 1981 and organized by the BTO and Irish Wildbird Conservancy) may become the norm. So you are free to experiment with a method. I use a "broad transect count", not along a straight line but along a route that dissects or abuts all the main habitats in my study area. Inevitably the counts are incomplete but they do allow direct comparison, the crux of year-on-year methods.

Assessing the accuracy of your counts

The ability of birds to hide is remarkable, but they will often stay in food-bearing habitat for quite some time. As you count them, you must resist the temptation to forsake your standard route or search area in order to obtain a full list on every visit. Remember that you are building up long-term data. For all the methods noted above, the best checks are provided by an expert companion who has experience of the CBC and like surveys.

In my opinion, it takes about three years to understand how birds exploit a piece of mixed habitat and about seven to observe all the regular fluctuations in a bird community caused by short term climate changes, general population trends and other external factors.

Sending in your results

Most ornithological reporting is done on an annual cycle. In Britain, for example, the BTO will want your CBC report at the end of the summer. It will be analysed by computer and become part of the national index of 59 species. Given its recent commitment to a winter atlas, the BTO will also be interested in your winter survey.

All your results should be summarised and sent to your local bird recorder or the regional organiser of national surveys. A task for the long nights of January! No need to faint at the prospect, however, as both the people just mentioned will give you plenty of advice on format and content. You must observe one golden rule – always list your notes on species in systematic order – and if you want to demonstrate particular events, send copies of your notes or counts as well. In this way, the various editors using your data will not miss the significant additions to knowledge that you have made.

Learning from bird books

Today there are thousands more active birdwatchers than there were 30 years ago. This increase in field activity has greatly increased our knowledge of birds. If you want to keep in touch and have a good background knowledge you will need to read widely. So here is a guide to the types of book and journal available (more details on page 63).

Stonechat

▲ **Typical field guide illustrations.**

Field guides
By now you will probably have bought a good "field guide". Field guides deal with identification. They contain illustrations of perched and flying birds and show various plumages of each species. The short text concentrates on information that will help identify the bird, giving details of size, plumage, calls, habitat and distribution. Some field guides cover all the birds of Europe, while others concentrate on British birds or a selection of the commonest species.

A field guide is one book that you must own, because without it you will find your way to the naming of families and species long and tortuous. Amongst the comprehensive Europe-wide guides, I suggest that you choose between "Peterson" and "Fitter" (to use their well-known nicknames). A useful guide to the commoner British species is Rob Hume's *Usborne Guide to Birds*, which is well illustrated with good pointers on identification.

Local bird reports
Detailed information on local birds will appear in the annual report published by the ornithological society or naturalists' trust of your county or province. If there is a birdwatchers' club in your nearest town they, too, will probably produce an annual report. These reports will contain a systematic list of dated occurrences and counts and (usually) some additional comments on weather, local population trends, local ringing results and rarity descriptions. These annual reports provide the closest, most detailed backcloth to your own observations and really are essential reading for any fact-collecting birdwatcher.

County ornithologies
By now most counties or provinces have also presented their ornithology in book or atlas form. Again these contain fully annotated lists of all the birds that have occurred within the region and narrative description of habitat, breeding population, migration and like subjects. Such a book gives you a historical appreciation of your local birds and, read with a map to hand, provides the quickest guide to the birds of an area unknown to you.

National journals
To add some national information to your local store, you should also read your country's journals of birdwatching. These appear periodically (usually monthly or quarterly)

and offer regular news about both birds and birdwatchers, summarized results of national surveys, identification papers and so on.

Handbooks

Many classic bird books have become scarce and expensive, but libraries can often help you find them. Do consult – or dip in and out of – your national ornithological handbook. Handbooks are large works containing all the available information on birds, from field characters to distribution, breeding, feeding and social behaviour. Start with the latest, for it should include the recent advances in knowledge and will firmly set your local ornithology in a broader context, but do not ignore earlier works. Of the latter, those written in the late 19th century are particularly interesting, for they illustrate how far birdwatching has advanced – in a nutshell, from shotgun to binoculars.

◀ The peregrine was the subject of a monograph by Derek Ratcliffe.

Monographs

Another classic kind of bird book is the monograph, a volume devoted entirely to just one family, species or ornithological subject. There is no better example than the bird volumes in "The New Naturalist" series, published by Collins. Within them, you will find the fullest possible treatment of birds as different as fulmar and hawfinch or tits and seabirds. Why not borrow several and understand how far-reaching bird study can be? In the same series, you can also find broader ecological texts. Of these, *The Natural History of The Highlands and Islands* (of Scotland) is a really inspiring book.

Narrative books

In your reading, you should also allow time for the vicarious enjoyment afforded by birdwatchers' and bird photographers' tales. Sadly this type of book is in decline but again your library should be able to resurrect titles by Sir Peter Scott, G. K. Yeates, and other authors of the less hurried postwar years. A particular favourite of mine is Robert Atkinson's *Island Going* but all such books are full of romping narrative *and* good practical advice.

Researching your local bird population

The first step is to obtain a copy of your regional ornithology and the last three annual bird reports that include records from your area. Read the book and scan the reports; then write a systematic list of the birds already known to exist in, or to visit, your area.

It makes sense to group your notes under the headings of breeding birds, winter visitors, regular migrants and vagrants; and to allow space for any marked habitat preferences, particularly local distributions and seasonal concentrations. In this way, you will have drawn the obvious ground rules for your own studies and marked the less obvious exceptions to them that will need special attention.

WHERE TO NEXT?

Do you want to specialize?

By now, you will have appreciated the main streams of birdwatching, in thought, study and practice. There are many options in these and I well remember how as a young observer I wandered among them. In the 1940s, egg collecting was not illegal and, like many of my generation, my first pursuits of birds were with that now forbidden aim in mind. Being a restless soul, however, I soon tired of looking for nests and, under the guidance of a gamekeeper, I began to see birds as a most beautiful part of the natural world and their migrations as their most exciting behaviour.

All through the 1950s, I was a besotted migration student and it was not until my 15th year as a birdwatcher that I realized how much more there was to study. This little piece of biography illustrates how easy it is to let birds rule your heart. There is nothing wrong with sheer enjoyment but I do wish that I had some of those years back.

So it will be worth your while to review your progress in birdwatching, after say eighteen months, and decide what you most want to do with your growing expertise. You may, of course, want to carry on dipping into a variety of birdwatching experiences. However, defining your special interests as early as possible could save you much later frustration.

The first step is to look at your birdwatching strengths and weaknesses. Is your sight more acute than most? Are your ears (sadly) less trustworthy? Do you enjoy the hunting most, or the gathering? Does some other personal interest or skill – such as mountaineering, foreign travel, art, photography or sound recording – complement your birdwatching and so allow an unusual study? Such questions deserve answers, and from these you can decide what you most want to do. You might go on, for example, to crack the stiffest identification tests, or test theoretically a mass of facts (and so prove a concept), or perhaps slog round a mountainous study area for ten consecutive holidays.

The fieldwork behind these projects will be interesting and often exciting because birds, wherever you are watching them, are unpredictable. Writing up your findings may be a bit tough but stick with it. Firm results are very satisfying.

The best birdwatchers and ornithologists that I know are all identifiable by their union of highly developed skills with unique interests and studies, all deployed against a wide knowledge of natural history.

Sorting out your interests will give you a real chance of finding a lasting enthusiasm and also an opportunity to contribute something of value to natural science.

"Twitching"

The most obvious (and expensive) cult in birdwatching nowadays is the mere assembly of a long life-list – the total number of different species seen. To extend their lists constantly, more and more young observers spend their time plugging into the grapevine of bird news, harvesting it for the most delectable rarity, obtaining its map reference and

Twitching – an excellent opportunity for close-up study of birdwatchers. The bird itself may prove more elusive...!

instantly tearing off after it.

"Twitching", as this all-go, often no-sleep behaviour is called, can be tremendous fun but do try to resist total seduction by it. Over-indulgence leads to frustration and all too often when the bird absents itself, all that ensues is a meaningless day of chat or distressing ornitho-political backbiting. Boring!

So try to take all the advice offered so far, and appreciate, for example, how the now common collared dove is just as exciting as the always rare bee-eater. In truth, the former's astonishingly explosive spread across Europe in this century is much more interesting than the latter's summer vagrancy. Try to bird-watch in the round, and you will find it more interesting.

Learning from other birdwatchers

The best short cut to the enjoyment of birds is to find a good ornithological friend. To find him you must seek out other birdwatchers, spot the expert among the just keen, and observe his skills and techniques. Then you simply ask for help.

The best way to get in touch with other birdwatchers is to join your local club or society. Its address and those of its main officers will be in the annual report (your lending library should have a copy). Don't be shy. Birdwatchers are a convivial lot and reserve a big welcome for new recruits. If you can show that you are also keen to take part, they will soon be asking for your help in local and even national cooperative surveys and studies.

Becoming a field ornithologist

Just when a keen birdwatcher becomes a field ornithologist is unclear. There is no exam to be passed and the change is marked more by a lasting increase in fact-gathering and summary than by passing success in rare bird hunting. To discover the full pleasures of field ornithology you will need to add some new skills to those you have already picked up in your early fieldwork. There are various places where you can go to see the skills of field ornithology in action. The rest of this section contains suggestions for three you can visit.

▼ Bramblings are one migratory species you may see at a bird observatory. They are winter visitors from Scandinavia.

Visiting a bird observatory

There is no more intensive ornithological experience – or better training – than that provided by a stay at a bird observatory.

These days most observatories apply broad, essentially scientific study techniques to all the birds in their area throughout the year. Increasingly they also monitor the fortunes of the rest of the local flora and fauna. So observatories present you with a marvellous chance to compare your knowledge with that of other observers, and to learn new or more advanced skills. Just a few days in the company of a helpful warden and other expert observers will teach you more than months of solitary watching.

Most bird observatories were set up principally to monitor migration, so they are generally located on coasts and islands. To get advice on which best accommodates the newcomer, you should again contact your local or national society officers. One of them will be bound to know the booking and travel arrangements and the best time to visit the observatory. Please note that, with few exceptions, bird observatories are devoted more to field study than to human comfort. So do not expect to be cossetted, and do read the joining instructions carefully.

Once at a bird observatory, try not to dash out on your own with eyes and binoculars all aglint for the first rarity. Stay close to the warden and initially pay as much attention to the study methods as to the birds themselves. During your visit you will be able to contribute to the counts of both grounded and flying birds, and help with concerted drives of birds into traps and nets. There will be a chance, too, to watch the handling of birds during ringing, and to closely examine plumage variation, and so on.

During the evenings, there will be a rollcall of the day's species, with discussions on types of migration or the variety of breeding birds and pointers, perhaps, on the identification of difficult species. As long as you stay awake, you will be learning, but do get some sleep. Dawn is always early and birds are at their busiest then. To get the most out of your stay, try to take notes not just on the birds but also on the study methods. These will give you numerous ideas for your own studies and future survey work.

Days at bird observatories are often long and full . . .
Scene 1 – Watching migrants at dawn.
Yellow wagtails
Scene 2 – Driving the Heligoland trap.
Scene 3 – Nesting peregrines can be seen at one observatory.
Scene 4 – Identifying a rare warbler before the sun goes down!

▼ If you can't get to an observatory, try to visit a ringing site to see ringers at work . . .

1. Taking birds from the net

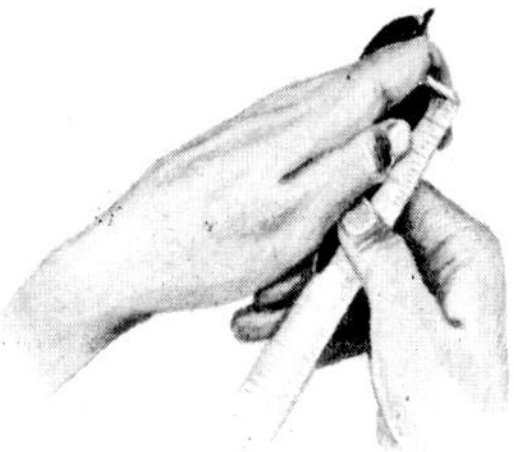

4. Measuring the bird

5. Weighing the bird by spring balance

2. Carrying the birds in bags to the ringing hut

Pied flycatcher

6. Releasing the bird

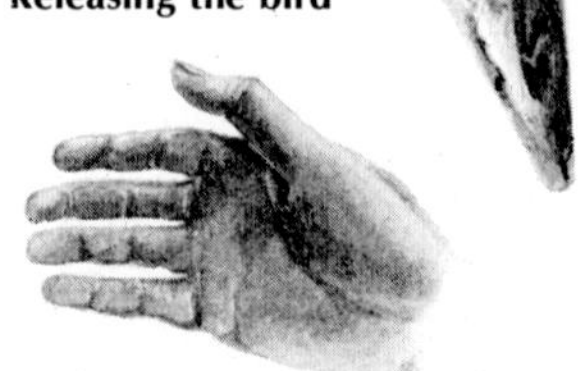

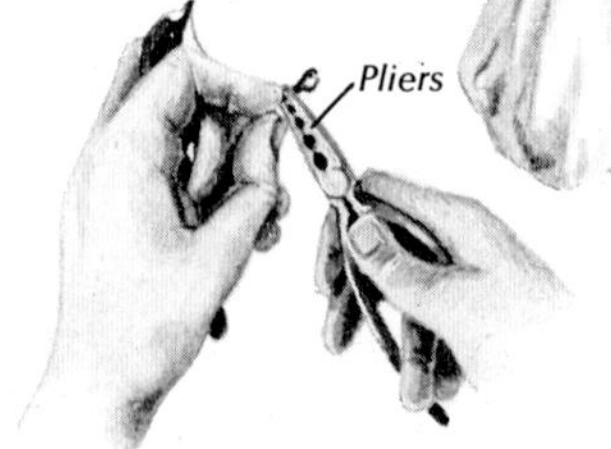

3. Ringing the bird

Visiting a ringing site

If you cannot get to a bird observatory, a visit to a site used by a group of ringers will give you a chance to observe the techniques of trapping and ringing.

Ringers are usually kept pretty busy, as their first duty is to release the birds quickly. So you may have to wait for answers to your questions. You can pick up a lot, though, by watching how they handle the birds and how they record the information they collect. Have a look, too, at the sites they pick for trapping and the species that turn up there. This will give you an idea of the population within a certain habitat and you may find one or two surprises.

Ringing groups work in a variety of habitats, often on inland sites. Local birdwatchers will know where your nearest group is based.

Visiting a bird museum

You will probably have been trailed past an exhibit of stuffed birds in your youth. Most of the specimens will have looked old (as they are, for the skins are often of birds shot 100 years ago), dusty, and – around the legs – brittle. Try to eradicate such memories and explore anew the greater treasures behind the museum's closed doors. Stored in the back rooms are thousands of skins, sorted geographically, and hundreds of reference books, shelved by subject.

To get behind the scenes in a museum can be a difficult exercise but do not be put off by the bureaucratic barriers. Insist that you are a genuine student and wish to increase your knowledge. Initially, I suggest that you keep your researches simple, for example the close examination of plumage colours and contours (feather sets) of a common species that you already know well, but later on, you could make them more complex. Only by spreading a range of skins along a museum bench can you see the wide range of sexual, seasonal and age differences that even a single species wears. Or you can examine the subtle changes in colour and patterns that mark geographical variation in birds and frequently merit the recognition of races or subspecies. These are subjects that relate to the taxonomy or classification of birds and to get a grasp of them, one day in a museum can be worth years of field study.

▲ Museum skins, showing considerable variation between the two European races of redpoll – lesser and mealy – and their close cousin the Arctic redpoll.

For information on observatories, ringing groups and museums contact your local library, local birdwatchers' club or get hold of a copy of Birdwatcher's Yearbook *(see page 62).*

Contributing to national records

So much happens in the world of birds every year that the ornithological records of Europe's nations will never be complete. The amateur can still carry out extremely useful studies. If you are worried about starting, just remember that all the leading observers of today had to begin somewhere. There's always something new to find.

The earlier sections in this book introduced you to some local and national study aims and methods. I hope that you will want to get involved in these but there are many other ways for you to contribute to your national ornithology.

My first published note was of a lesser yellowlegs in southern Scotland in the spring of 1950 (see the illustrations opposite). Then it was exceptional for an American wader to appear in that season, and the editors of *British Birds* (see page 63) considered the bird worthy of the national news. Nowadays the record would not merit full publication but there will always be others that do.

How you can contribute

You can best judge the types of record and study to which the amateur contributes from your own reading and the comments of a helpful expert.

In order of current popularity (but not necessarily scientific merit), amateurs contribute in four main areas. You can (1) submit rare bird records to your national review body, (2) offer your own perceptions of field characters (identification points) to the relevant national journal, (3) report on unusual behaviour, or (4) summarise significant results from your surveys or studies.

The last may range widely and can represent the most permanent and enjoyable products of your birdwatching. Working with others I have recently helped to redefine the seabird passage off eastern Britain. Right now I am bursting to investigate the winter feeding behaviour of the redpoll. No-one else has and it is just this sort of study that allows you to compete with the professional.

Writing up your results

The illustrations opposite show how two friends and I explored the sighting of the lesser yellowlegs and turned the observation into a published "note". Short "notes" are the best way to present a single observation on behaviour or identification.

Multiple observations of any kind may require a longer write-up, "Reports", for instance, deal systematically with such subjects as the bird life of a region (your local bird report, for example). "Papers" examine at length particular pieces of research and survey work.

Preparing the notes, reports and papers that will turn the raw data in your notebooks and logs into well written conclusions requires some dedication. Well directed efforts will be constructively criticised by ornithological editors. They will be happy to give advice, in the form of examples of writing construction, a list of other literary references, and so on.

To avoid disappointment, there are three golden rules. First make sure that you have something new or significantly different to contribute. Second, demonstrate that you have researched your subject fully. Third, never over-reach in deduction or conclusion – and be prepared to revise a conclusion if need be.

Discovery and observation ▶
While enjoying the common waders of Aberlady Bay on 13th May 1950, three young observers flush a "small greenshank" but are very puzzled by its yellow legs and square white rump. It is clearly a rarity but which? They watch the wader closely, making notes.

Lesser Yellowlegs
very tapering
white square
long legs, visible behind tail in flight
Redshank
rather shorter legs
fairly blunt

◀ *Noting unusual features*
The bird's size is difficult to judge, since its wings and legs are both proportionately longer than those of a redshank nearby. It also lacks the "round-shouldered" walk of that species and has a slower more buoyant flight. These points are stressed in the notes and help to identify the bird as a lesser yellowlegs from America!

Tracing the bird's origin ▶
In the early fifties, no-one fully understood how widely some American waders strayed in spring. Searching the weather records the observers find that there were strong westerly gales in late April. Perhaps the bird was windblown across the North Atlantic and Scotland at that time.

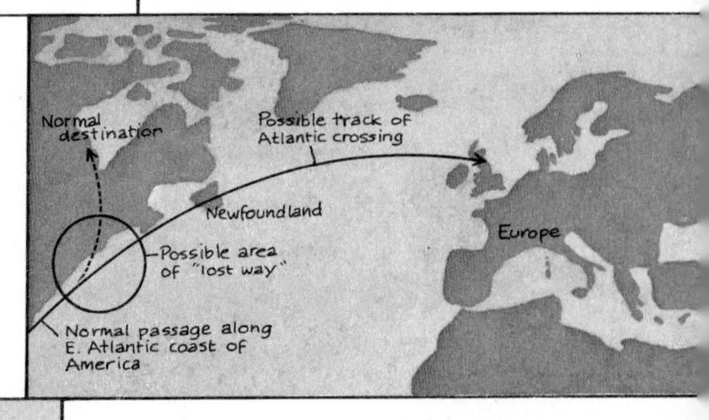

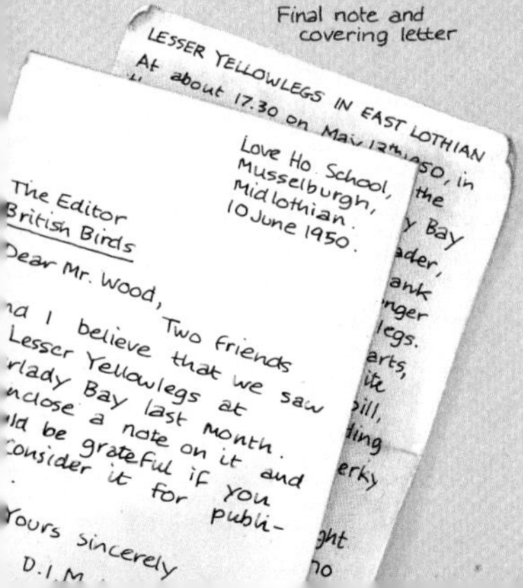

LESSER YELLOWLEGS IN EAST LOTHIAN
At about 17.30 on May 13th 1950, in ... the ... y Bay ... ader, ... ank ... nger ... legs. ... arts, ... ite ... bill, ... ding ... erky ... ght ... no

Love Ho. School,
Musselburgh,
Midlothian.
10 June 1950.

The Editor
British Birds

Dear Mr. Wood,

... nd I believe that we saw ... Lesser Yellowlegs at ... rlady Bay last month. ... nclose a note on it and ... ld be grateful if you ... consider it for publi- ...

Yours sincerely
D. I. M.

◀ *Publication of a note*
On behalf of their school ornithological society, the observers write up a "note". This follows the style of other notes in *British Birds* and is submitted to the Editor. It is accepted by the national expert on the species and in December 1950 is published, becoming a piece of Britain's ornithological history. (See *British Birds*, Vol. 43, p.406).

Getting wider experience

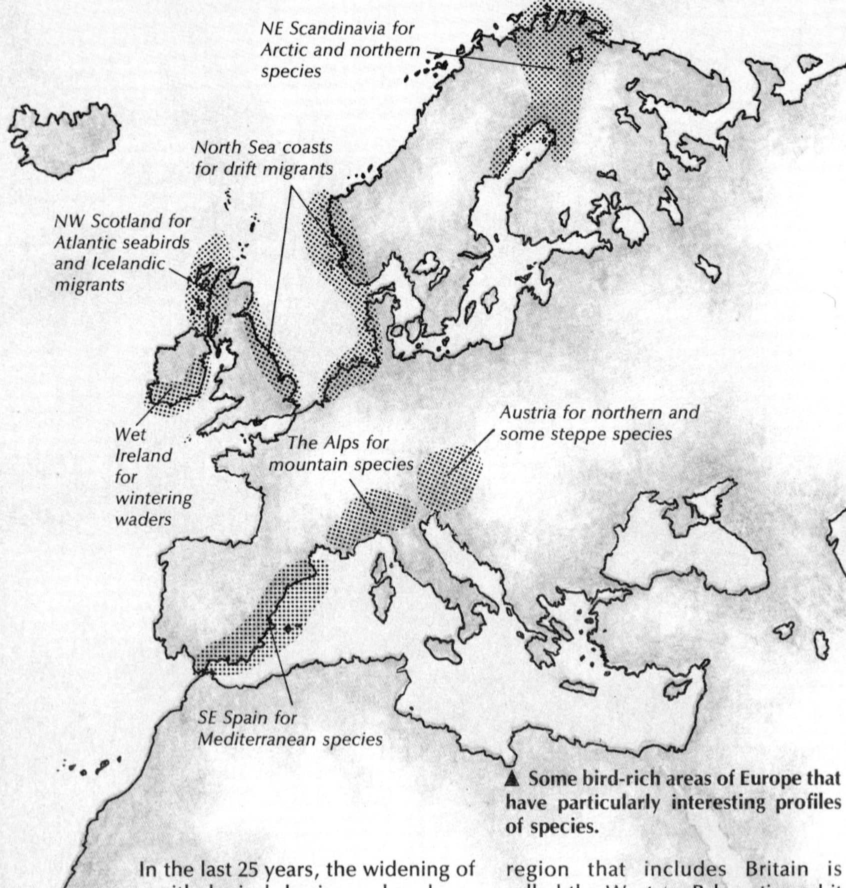

▲ Some bird-rich areas of Europe that have particularly interesting profiles of species.

In the last 25 years, the widening of ornithological horizons has been dramatic. Bird books, journals and magazines have made more and more references to events abroad; packaged holidays and expeditions have sent birdwatchers all over the world; and natural scientists now look at broad faunal regions (large areas of the world which have breeding species in common) rather than just individual countries. The faunal region that includes Britain is called the Western Palearctic and it covers Europe and adjacent areas of Africa and the Middle East.

For me, the fact that Europe has a list of breeding species whose distribution may range from "widespread" to "local" is very exciting. Naturally, parts of Europe have habitats quite different from those found in the British Isles, so amongst your familiar species you will find

Several East European species can be seen on the steppe (grassland plains) of Austria's eastern border.

Large numbers of geese fly from their Arctic breeding grounds to winter in west Scotland.

others that are new to you. For example, in Spanish maquis (sharp, hillside scrub), you may find woodchat shrike and black-eared wheatear alongside the more familiar kestrel and stonechat.

I know of no more fascinating travel experience than to see the changes in passing countryside and to spot the birds that signpost the different habitats within the whole. By visiting the regions of Europe that have particularly interesting profiles of species, you will begin to understand the inter-relationships of your own birds more fully.

Take a close look at the distribution maps and habitat notes in your field guide and handbook before you select a route or a centre for overseas observations. In the meantime, the map on page 52 will show you the explorations that have taught me most about the distribution of European birds. I have not yet been to Yugoslavia and Greece but expeditions there are worthwhile.

Getting a wider experience of birds will give you a fuller understanding of their distribution, the habitat preferences of individual species and the overlaps in habitat selection that allow their communities to mix.

Looking at the different ranges of species within Europe

In Europe, the last of the Ice Ages retreated 10,000 years ago but its effects are still detectable.

By travelling along a SW/NE line in western Europe and a N/S one in eastern Europe, you can virtually roll back time and sense the shifts in range of Arctic, Continental, Temperate and Mediterranean species. A good example of such a feature is the so-called "chaffinch/brambling line" which runs across northern Scandinavia. South and west of it, the chaffinch (a Continental species) exploits most treed habitats and is resident in much of Europe. North of it only the brambling (a sub-Arctic species) is adapted to living in the few deciduous trees of the northern conifer forests but it stays only to breed, moving south in winter.

▼ Spain's hot, dry climate attracts Mediterranean species that can also be found in North Africa.

Taking a break

Taking an occasional break from your usual birdwatching studies, however fascinating, is important. A day's expedition to a bird-rich area will provide some exciting moments and seeing new species in different habitats should set your mind thinking. Here, then, are a few ideas of places to go for some great birdwatching moments.

▲ **Whooper swans on a misty morning.**

Visiting a wildfowl refuge

There is no more inspiring sight than herds of wildfowl strewn across a wide sky or scattered through an ancient wetland. Happily, western Europe (and its Atlantic climate) offers many chances to see winter assemblies of ducks, geese and swans that have flown from breeding grounds as distant as Siberia.

In Britain, one of the most evocative – and certainly the most educational – places to watch wildfowl is at Slimbridge, the home of the Wildfowl Trust on the uppermost reach of the Severn Estuary. Slimbridge has both a tame wildfowl collection and hordes of wild birds. So if your head is turned by the gaggles of wild geese or the whistles of wigeon, this is the place for you.

Once you have used its excellent hides and double-checked your identification of wild birds against their tame cousins in the nearby collection, you will be well prepared to explore the many other winter wetlands of Britain and Ireland. Their list is long, for example, north Norfolk and the Wash, the Essex estuaries, Poole Harbour (excellent for grebes), and the Wexford Slobs. So your winter expeditions need never lack variety of species and scene.

Wandering through a southern woodland

Few wooded habitats in central and southern Europe have been left undisturbed, and finding one that has kept its ancestral flora and fauna is not easy. Birdwatching in an ancient wood is however a special experience worth a long journey.

In Britain and Ireland, the forests that sprang up after the Ice Age have been almost totally destroyed but there are a few isolated patches left. The best in terms of bird life is the New Forest and there in a long summer day you can still see strong glimmers of the diversity of species once common to all lowland England. In fact, a wander through its groves and across its heaths is the nearest to a truly European birdwatching experience that a British observer can have.

During your walk, look out particularly for birds of prey. Two scarce species may appear overhead at any time. They are the lithe hobby and the strange, wasp-eating honey buzzard. Among the gorse, watch out for the Dartford warbler, Britain's only resident among that normally migratory tribe.

Other pieces of broad-leaved forests are scattered around England and even those close to cities may support some surprising birds. The one that I know best is Epping Forest, near London, which is an excellent place for all three woodpeckers, the elusive hawfinch and – once to date – the mysterious short-toed treecreeper, widespread in Europe but with its true status over here a series of question marks. A glance at a map will soon reveal your nearest dense wood. Do go and enjoy it.

▼ The New Forest's heathlands and its oak, beech and pine woods harbour some interesting species.

Exploring a reedmarsh

The last patches of ancient fenland and marsh are, like the old woods, widely scattered and still threatened. Luckily conservationists have recently given them much attention and some of these bird-rich communities are open to you and me. Huge reedbeds make for difficult birdwatching. So if you are to revel fully in it, take your time: a true case of waiting and seeing.

The most famous bird reserve in Britain is also the nation's most splendid marsh – Minsmere in Suffolk. To get into its magic hides, you must first join the RSPB (see page 62) and then wait patiently for your entry permit. I do advise you to do both, however, for Minsmere on a late spring or early summer day can be breathtaking. Below is my account of one short visit there.

▲ **Bearded tits are totally adapted to living in reedbeds.**

21 May 1972
An early morning at Minsmere

I didn't bother with sleep and drove straight from the end of the late film to East Bridge, arriving at 0345. It was still dark; so I moved on to Dunwich and drove slowly along the heath lanes. On the end one, I ran slap into not one but at least three nightjars – all glowing red eyes and winking white wing panels in my headlights – and I was smiling – before dawn – at such an unexpected gift.

It's always good to start with a surprise. I took a look from the sandcliff but the light was still poor. So I went back towards East Bridge, fancying a walk along the stream rather than the usual plod across the shingle strand. Every pause made on the overland lane produced several nightingales in full song. One was literally only a few feet from the car window and I could hear the growls and grace notes as well as the pulsing crescendos. More magic!

Down at the bridge, the dawn was beginning to break and I struck out east. A heavy dew and Suffolk nettles combined to make my progress a soggy and stinging experience but it mattered little, as a drake garganey fluttered up, snipe drummed and sedge warblers chortled everywhere. My adrenalin continued to flow. Canada geese with young broods in the nearby ditch honked furiously at my passing but suddenly a much more exciting sound reached my ears. It was a continuous reeling and could only be coming from a grasshopper warbler or a much rarer Savi's warbler. The bird – or was it two? – lead me something of a stationary dance but, at last, patience paid off. It shuffled up a taller reed and a clear view showed that it was indeed a Savi's. Hardly believing my luck, I moved on with the sight of the morning's

Some of Minsmere's avian gems 21 May 1972

first marsh harrier and the calls of bittern and avocet spurring my legs.

Given the grapevine news, I wasn't surprised to find the public shorehide already tenanted and the nearest reserve hide obviously guarded. Indeed there was a distinct air of ornithological siege. Squeezing in amongst several friends, I soon learnt that they had the broad-billed sandpiper in view. Given the crush and tension, it was not until I borrowed a telescope that I was certain of it. Contrary to its book image, it was dashing about and feeding actively like its dunlin companions!

Of the main target – an almost mythical terek sandpiper – there was no sign, and after an hour I became restless. So I went back to the bridge, getting superb views of a bittern and the cock marsh harrier but not hearing the Savi's again.

Back at East Bridge I was treated to the astonishing sight of a snipe perched on a telegraph wire and I also took the opportunity to brush up on reed warblers. Since the last of their tribe that I had studied were paddyfield and Blyth's reed warbler in Baluchistan five weeks before, the comparison was most useful.

Snatching a traditional pork pie and apple snack on the way, I circled back to the cliff car park – picking up a beautiful cock red-backed shrike on the way – and moved along to the shore for a second stare at the Scrape. The besieging forces had grown and the latest news on the terek had been acquired from a tetchy warden. "Still here – but in a hidden pool!" A difficult time ensued and I soon gave up the hides for wandering along the coast, picking up six black-tailed godwits, a Kentish plover, a late pintail, and the usual terns, and just enjoying the place itself.

At 0830 I went back into the hide near the sluice and pulled my concentration back together. A wandering stint was confirmed as a Temminck's, and hardly had it been noted when a voice yelled out "What's this?!" Bent double, I peered out and there, scampering about with classic gallop, was the terek sandpiper. I rushed out to spread the word but the fickle bird immediately returned to its sanctuary. So sadly many others were disappointed. Never mind, I had had a splendid morning's birds and could speed home quite untroubled!

◀ The author's illustration of some highlights in a morning's birdwatching at Minsmere in Suffolk.

Other ideas

The suggestions above have directed you to three great natural spectacles and described a visit to one of them. There are many other places to visit (some are listed on pages 60–61) and you will probably discover your own favourite spots.

Great birdwatching moments are not confined to bird reserves and observatories. It can be an exciting experience, for example, to watch the aerial floods of birds coming to a roost or passing along a hillside or headland, or to find newly-come migrants hiding in foggy coastal bushes after a night of east wind.

Sewage farms, incidentally, should not be forgotten, with their mass of chattering starlings, pied wagtails and gulls by the hundred, and always the possibility of an unusual wader.

If it is the odd rarity that beckons you, then a long trip to Fair Isle or Scilly will provide the best odds on such. There you will find the north and south-west poles of British ornithology, hordes of the keenest observers and more uncommon birds than anywhere else in Europe!

THE BIRDWATCHER'S ROUND

Reserves and bird observatories

In spite of the marked habitat losses of the last two centuries, there are happily many bird haunts that have been saved and a growing few that have been created. There follows a selection of those that present the most exciting ornithological pageants. Fuller lists have been published in *Birdwatcher's Yearbook* and *Where to Watch Birds*, both listed on pages 62–63.

SCOTLAND

Sands of Forvie and Ythan Estuary (NCC), Grampian. Take A975 to Newburgh, north of Aberdeen; park in spaces provided and take note of seasonal changes of access. Habitats range from huge sand dunes to long muddy estuary; birds include largest British colony of eiders, four species of terns and a winter circus of grey geese.

Loch Garten (RSPB) and Loch an Eilean (NCC); Highlands. Take side roads, respectively north-east and south-east of Aviemore; park in spaces provided and keep to paths or nature trail. Closely adjacent areas providing access to heart of Scotland's most ancient forests; birds include the famous ospreys, the majestic capercaillie, crossbill and crested tit. Access to nearby Cairngorm Mountains by ski lift.

Fair Isle, Shetland. To visit, contact the Warden, Fair Isle Bird Observatory, By Lerwick, Shetland. Large, encliffed, oceanic island; breeding birds include skuas, twite and endemic Fair Isle wren; migrants include more rarities than anywhere else in Europe. A *locus classicus* for all keen birdwatchers.

WALES

Cors Tregaron (NCC), Dyfed. Approach by A485 and B4343 north of Tregaron; park carefully and do not stray from signed path; best watching is of "wait and see" type. Example of raised peat bog, surrounded by upland farms and wooded hillsides; birds include wintering red kites, buzzards, grasshopper warblers and lesser redpolls.

Lake Vyrnwy (RSPB), Powys. Encircled by B4393; park carefully and keep to nature trail. Upland lake surrounded by woods; breeding birds range from goosander to redstart and pied flycatcher.

Bardsey Island, off Gwynedd. To visit the observatory, contact the Booking Secretary, 21a Gestridge Road, Kingsteignton, Newton Abbot, Devon (0626) 68580. 450 acre island, supporting breeding Manx shearwaters, storm petrels and choughs, and often receiving large falls of night migrants; rarities always of special interest.

ENGLAND

Bempton Cliffs (RSPB), Yorkshire. Approach along B1255 from Bridlington, turning north-west in Flamborough and north at Bempton; park at end of lane and tread carefully along cliff edge. Habitat essentially the north face of Britain's eastern cape, supporting the only mainland colony of gannets, thousands of auks and hundreds of thousands of kittiwakes.

Blakeney Point, Cley and Salthouse (National Trust and Norfolk Naturalists' Trust), Norfolk. Skirted by A149, in places winding and narrow, so drive carefully and park only in spaces provided. Habitats range from sand and shingle to saltings and reedbeds and are probably the most searched of any in Britain; local list contains over 300 species, with shore larks, snow buntings and brent geese in winter, a chance of any marsh species in summer and regular falls of many migrants in spring and autumn. Together with the woods of Wells-next-the-sea, these are the best migrant haunts in England and excellent training grounds for young observers.

Stodmarsh (NCC), Kent. Approach by A257 from Canterbury, then by side road to Stodmarsh; park carefully and walk north to marsh wall. Habitat essentially a huge freshwater marsh, extended by winter flooding; birds include resident Cetti's warbler, winter wildfowl and summer visitors to reedbed, notably sedge, reed and grasshopper warblers. Many garganey appear in spring.

Poole Harbour and surround, Dorset. Approach by various routes. Harbour best in winter, with black-tailed godwits, small grebes and saw-billed ducks nowhere more obvious in England. Relict heaths subject to strict conservation and restricted access but still give good chance of stonechat and even Dartford warbler on reserve edges. Excellent area for birdwatching holiday in any season.

Martin Mere (Wildfowl Trust), Lancashire. Watch for signs on A59 at Burscough Bridge and A565 at Mere Brow; park as indicated and enjoy wide range of amenities and spectacle, which now rival those at Slimbridge. Birds include up to 18,000 pink-footed geese, hen harriers and merlin in winter and an excellent variety of waders all year.

Dungeness (RSPB), Kent. Approach through Lydd, aiming at the nuclear power stations, inland of which is the bird observatory (easternmost cottage within shingle "moat") and its trapping area. To the north lie various gravel pits, some managed as reserves. Beware wandering into shelling range. Habitat unique, with shifting shingle base and huge patches of gorse, brambles and stunted trees, often flooded. Birds include lowest level breeding wheatears in Britain, occasional floods of migrants and fascinating passage of seabirds, notably little gull and marsh terns. The best station to observe modern bird-trapping techniques.

IRELAND

Wexford Wildfowl Reserve (IWC), Co. Wexford. Approach from Wexford, with side roads to either North or South Slob. Habitat essentially wet, flat farmland surrounding natural inlet with Sandy Island. Birds include roseate tern in summer and thousands of white-fronted geese in winter, the latter picking up fellow travellers as rare as snow goose and the wild small races of Canada goose.

Cape Clear, Co. Cork. To visit the observatory, contact the Booking Secretary, 46 The Glen, Boden Park, Dublin 14. Large, rocky, rolling island off one of Ireland's south-western capes; birds include breeding chough and black guillemot and many vagrants, particularly trans-atlantic ones, but main study is of oceanic passages in July and August, annually featuring great and Cory's shearwaters.

National societies

Your choice of national society membership will depend on your interests but all of the following deserve at least your occasional support.

British Trust for Ornithology (BTO), Beech Grove, Station Road, Tring, Herts HP23 5NR. Tel: (044-282) 3461. Harnesses the fieldwork of amateurs for conservation-oriented studies organised by itself and other national organisations; also administers the national ringing scheme and most of the major bird observatories. Publishes *BTO News* and quarterly journal *Bird Study*, plus highly informative guides on many subjects, ranging from taxonomy to migration periods.

Field Studies Council (FSC), Preston Montford, Montford Bridge, Shrewsbury, Shropshire SY4 1HW. Tel: (0743) 850674. Aims to improve appreciation of natural world for any student, organising short courses on many natural history subjects. Publishes *Field Studies*.

Irish Wildbird Conservancy (IWC), c/o Royal Irish Academy, 19 Dawson Street, Dublin 2, Ireland. Coordinates and leads all birdwatching studies in Ireland, liaising with government on conservation. Publishes *IWC News* and *Irish Birds*, plus informative booklets.

Royal Society for the Protection of Birds (RSPB), The Lodge, Sandy, Bedfordshire SG19 2DL. Tel: (0767) 80551. Manfully protects Britain's bird habitats and their common and uncommon inhabitants; enthuses and educates over 340,000 members and opinion leaders; reacts to all current and future threats to birds. Publishes *Birds*, special reports, and wide range of birdwatching aids; makes excellent films.

World Wildlife Fund (WWF), Panda House, 11–13 Ockford Road, Godalming, Surrey GU7 1QU. Puts together international awareness of threats to natural world and endangered species, and generates widespread support for corrective measures, including cash grants for reserves. Publishes *World Wildlife News* and *World Wildlife Yearbook*.

Young Ornithologists' Club (YOC). Address as RSPB. Enthuses and guides over 111,000 birdwatchers under 18, providing training and study opportunities. Publishes *Bird Life*.

Books and journals

Here is a short list of books. It includes those mentioned in the preceding text and others that you can seek out in bookshops or libraries. Libraries should be able to find out-of-print titles.

INTRODUCTIONS TO BIRDWATCHING

Discover Birds Ian Wallace (Whizzard Press/André Deutsch 1979). Generally acknowledged as the most evocative introduction published in recent years.

Birdwatcher's Yearbook 1981 (published annually since then). John E. Pemberton (Buckingham Press 1980). Packed with useful facts, references and details of reserves, observatories, local clubs and national societies; shortens the beginner's search to all sorts of things ornithological.

FIELD GUIDES

Usborne Guide to Birds of Britain & Europe Rob Hume (Usborne 1981). Well-illustrated guide to a selection of common species.

The Mitchell Beazley Birdwatcher's Pocket Guide Peter Hayman (Mitchell Beazley 1979). Slim, wallet-sized guide to common and regular species.

A Field Guide to the Birds of Britain and Europe R. Peterson, G. Mountfort and P. A. D. Hollom (Collins 1954, revised edition 1982). Classic field guide, with the best illustrations and text of all – but less comprehensive than the next title.

The Birds of Britain and Europe with North Africa and the Middle East H. Heinzel, R. Fitter and J. Parslow (Collins 1972). The best alternative to "Peterson" with a useful series of maps.

SCIENTIFIC HANDBOOKS

The Handbook of British Birds H. F. Witherby, F. C. R. Jourdain, N. F. Ticehurst and B. W. Tucker (Witherby 1938). The most influential handbook ever published and still the best reference to all but rare birds.

The Popular Handbook of British Birds P. A. D. Hollom (Witherby 1952). Condensed version of above five-volume work.

DISTRIBUTION OF BRITISH BIRDS

The Atlas of Breeding Birds in Britain and Ireland J. T. R. Sharrock (T. & A. D. Poyser for BTO/IWC 1976). Maps and discusses the breeding distribution and population trends of all British and Irish breeding birds; best yet example of how birdwatching becomes field ornithology.

LIST OF BIRDWATCHING SITES

Where to Watch Birds John Gooders (André Deutsch 1967, Pan 1977). Full details of approach route to and birds within Britain's major birdwatching stations.

GOOD READS

Seventy years of birdwatching H. G. Alexander (T. & A. D. Poyser 1974). Fascinating echoes of 20th century field ornithology across the world.

Island Going R. Atkinson (Collins 1949). Enjoyable account of seaborne expeditions after seabirds.

Natural History in the Highlands and Islands (of Scotland) Frank Fraser Darling (Collins 1949). Inspiring survey of the fauna and flora of an ancient region, with full discussion of Man's assault upon it.

Bill Oddie's Little Black Bird Book W. E. Oddie (Eyre Methuen 1980). Hilarious, bubble-bursting review of modern birdwatching – and particularly birdwatchers' behaviour.

Bird Haunts in Northern Britain G. K. Yeates (Faber and Faber 1948). Excellent example of bird photographer's work and travels in post-war period.

Birdwatching in the Seventies Ian Wallace (Macmillan 1981). Summarises major bird and birdwatching events in each season of the 1970s.

PERIODIC JOURNALS

Birds RSPB members' quarterly magazine. Lavishly illustrated, topical news of birds and their protection.

British Birds Monthly by annual subscription (enquiries to: BB Circulation, Fountains, Park Lane, Blunham, Bedford MK44 3NJ). Central, topical voice of British birdwatching and field ornithology, with best content balance of all journals.

INDEX

Where species are illustrated, the page number appears in *italics*.